CONTEMPORARY MATH

CONTEMPORARY MATH

by Frank Clark

Franklin Watts, Inc.
575 Lexington Avenue, New York 22

I am grateful to the following for their help in the preparations for this book:

Alan Vorwald, Barbara Silverglate, and Ralph J. Oravec for his suggestions and his editing of chapters 7, and 8.

Library of Congress Catalog Card Number 64-12131

Printed in the United States of America

2 3 4 5

CONTENTS

INTRODUCTION

As THE SPACE CAPSULE returns from its journey around Mars, the astronaut prepares to fire the retro-rockets that will prepare his re-entry into the earth's atmosphere. The capsule's radio is transmitting a staggering amount of computations on speed, yaw, orbital path, radiation, meteorites, temperature of the nose cone, geodetic data, and the physical condition of the astronaut.

Information races back to the tracking stations around the earth and is literally poured into electronic computers. No amount of human clerical help could possibly copy down all these facts, sort them out, and analyze them in the split second of time it takes to make crucial decisions on the astronaut's flight.

New concepts in mathematics are needed to help these computers in their rapid calculations. For example, what was once an abstract system of numeration, now fits in these electronic devices as easily as the decimal system of numbers "fits" our ten fingers.

This practical tool for electronic problem solving is the binary system of numbers, which uses only two symbols, 1 and 0, for counting.

DECIMAL:	0	1	2	3	4	5	6	7	8	9
BINARY:	0	1	10	11	100	101	110	111	1000	1001

The binary system of numeration is only one of several mathematical concepts that are being used in electronic calculations. Scientists and statisticians must determine the truth of propositions about chemical elements and compounds, about matter and energy, about soil and its nutrients, and even about plants and animals. Boolean algebra, an algebra that deals with classes of objects, helps our scientists determine the truth about propositions by using the science of logic.

The principles of this algebra of objects and logic can now be applied to modern systems of electronic gates and switches. It is something like sending a set of electric trains over different roads of track, only much more complex. Boolean algebra is only one of many abstract principles, once leisurely discussed by theorists in ivory towers, which have suddenly become vital and important to the practical, problem-solving men of our own times.

Today's mathematicians are interested in discovering properties of numbers which can frequently be used for short cuts in computations. For example: New testing procedures that measure the talents of students and job applicants use special techniques in statistical computations to evaluate this special type of data.

Another property of numbers is used in the technique called Speed Arithmetic. With a minimum of time and pencil work, executives and statisticians often use Speed Arithmetic to make fast calculations at conferences, or even during a short phone call.

Thus, we should not find it too unusual that the activities of modern businessmen, the education and training of engineers, chemists, doctors, or even average citizens, have been greatly changed by the improvement of these new mathematical techniques.

Indeed, man has always found an urgency in his calculations and has usually devised a method to meet his needs. Cave men, Egyptians, Romans, sailors, merchants, and scientists have all experienced this necessity for making accurate calculations. They have all been curious and creative in their approach, inventing such things as numeration systems, a sand and pebble counter, the abacus, the cash register, and today's computer.

If we are really to understand contemporary mathematics, we must go back into history and have a brief look at our earliest ancestors to see how they solved the necessary and pressing computation problems of their times.

Chapter One

THE DECIMAL SYSTEM

A SENSE OF NUMBERS seems to be present in many living things. Wasps, birds, and some species of animals possess this faculty in a very limited way. Unlike other forms of life, man was able to develop this number sense into an ability to count and measure his surroundings.

One explanation of how this may have happened is seen in finger counting — something all of us do at times. When our earliest ancestors found objects they wanted to count, they probably used their fingers because they were so convenient. Since they rarely went about unarmed, they tucked the weapon under one arm (probably the left) and made a one-to-one correspondence between their fingers and the objects they were counting, using the free right hand as the check-off hand. Perhaps this explains why right-handed people almost always use their left hands for counting.

It is easy to see how man himself was actually the first computer. His fingers provided a sort of mechanical device and, as today's computer does, he even "printed up" the results of his counting. These markings can still be seen on the walls of prehistoric caves. Many of these signs have a great similarity. The signs for 1, for example, are symbols that apparently represent an uplifted finger.

Roman numerals, which are used only for limited purposes in our own times, show traces of finger counting. V, the symbol for five, probably represents the gap between the thumb and fingers, and X suggests two V's for ten. To represent four, the Romans used IV, a symbol that suggests the process of subtraction when the smaller number is placed to the left of the larger. When the position of these symbols is reversed to VI, the smaller number is placed to the right of the larger, and the process of addition takes place.

As trading and shopkeeping became more complicated, man needed a device that would record information, perform an arithmetic operation, and quickly come up with accurate answers. Finger counting was too limited and Roman numerals too cumbersome.

One of the earliest devices man invented to do his counting for him was the abacus. On the abacus it was possible to substitute beads for fingers. The abacus became such a dependable instrument for counting that it is still used in many parts of the world today.

To understand how an abacus works, we can build one of our own that uses ten beads in each column. Get a strip of wood about 3½ feet long, ½ inch wide, and about ¼ inch thick. Cut two lengths of 1 foot each, and two other lengths of 8 inches each. Tack or nail them together in a rectangle as shown in the illustration.

Now tack five 9-inch lengths of picture wire on the inside of the top strip of wood. On each wire put ten beads or buttons. Then attach the loose ends of the five wires to the inside of the bottom strip of wood. About 4 inches from the bottom of the frame, tack another wire across the face of the frame and push all the beads above this wire. The ten beads on the wire of the abacus represent our ten fingers.

Each bead on the wire farthest to the right represents one.

Each bead on the second wire is worth ten ones, or 10. Each bead on the third wire is worth ten tens, or 100, and so on.

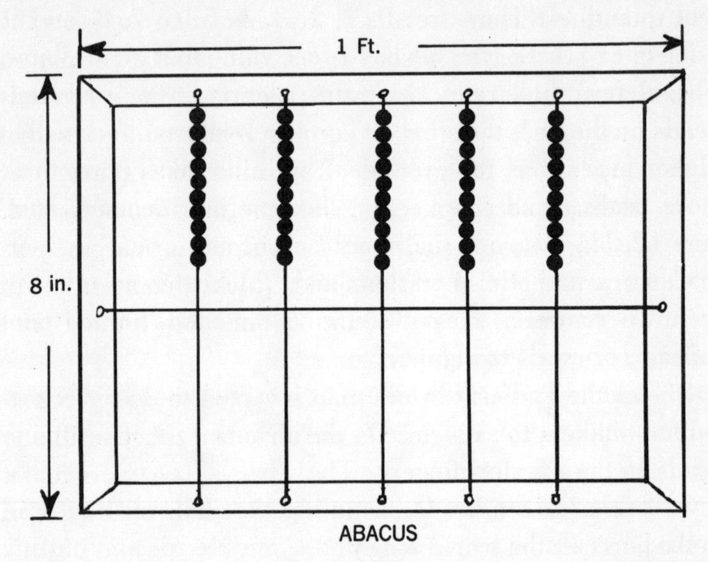

ABACUS

The system of counting or reckoning by ten is called the *decimal system;* because we have ten beads on each wire, our homemade abacus is therefore a decimal abacus.

Move down four beads on the first wire to represent 4. Push them back up and move down four beads on the second wire. Are we still representing 4? No! Even though the same number of beads have been moved, the number represented now is 40. This is because the beads on the second wire are in the tens place. What number would we be representing if we moved down four beads on the hundreds wire? Or if we moved down four beads on the tens wire and three beads on the ones wire, what number would be represented?

The wire on which the beads are placed shows *place* value. Four beads can have different place values, for example 4 and 40, according to the place we select for them.

In the decimal system we use a set of symbols to represent quantities. They are: 0, 1, 2, 3, 4, 5, 6, 7, 8, and 9. Each one of these symbols has a *face* value that we all know. The abacus illustrates this very clearly. We used four beads on the ones wire for 4. To represent a number with a higher face value, for example 7, we must push down three more beads on the ones wire. Can you represent the numbers 12, 56, 396, and 7,216 on the abacus?

Can you add 8 + 4 on the abacus? Yes, this way:

1. To represent 8, pull down eight beads in the ones column, or on the ones wire.

2. Add 4. The next two beads you pull down in the ones column make a total of 10. You still have to add two more beads in the ones column.

3. Exchange ten beads in the ones column for one bead in the tens column by pushing up the ones beads and pulling down one bead in the tens column.

4. Add the remaining two beads in the ones column. The abacus now shows 1 ten and 2 ones, which is 12.

Clear the abacus of this problem by moving all beads up.

Try subtracting:

$$\begin{array}{r} 46 \\ -14 \\ \hline \end{array}$$

1. Show the number 46 with six beads in the ones column and four beads in the tens column (4 tens + 6 ones = 46).

2. Subtract 14. First push four beads up in the ones column. This leaves two beads in the ones column.

3. Push one bead up in the tens column. You have two beads in the ones column and three beads in the tens column. Your answer is 32.

Now subtract: 42
−27

1. Show 42 on the abacus by pushing down two beads in the ones column and four beads in the tens column.

2. Take 7 ones from 42 by pushing up the two beads in the ones column and counting, "One, two."

3. Push up one bead in the tens column and push down ten beads in the ones column; you have exchanged 1 ten for 10 ones.

4. Counting then continues from step 2: Count "Three, four, five, six, seven," as you push five beads up in the ones column. You have now subtracted a total of 7 from 42. You have five beads left in the ones column.

5. Now subtract 2 tens by pushing up two beads in the tens column. You now have one bead in the tens column and five beads in the ones column. Your answer is 15.

Now try to solve the following problems on your own. Remember, each bead in the first column on the right represents 1, in the next column each bead represents ten ones, or 10, in the third column each bead represents ten tens, or 100.

418	638	629	813	713
+237	+763	−417	−569	−613

The success of the abacus is due to a clear and accurate performance in answering the question: How many? It is a practical and dependable device that met the mathematical needs of ancient times.

Later the straight line of the abacus was put into a circle.

The beads were replaced by notches on a wheel, and rapid calculations were made by the wheels and gears of adding machines. Cash registers and desk calculators are examples of these wheel-and-gear counters.

ZERO—THE EMPTY COLUMN

We have used the symbol 0 several times now, and in our last problem on the abacus we arrived at two empty columns. The written answer for this problem was 100. Zero is a concept we take for granted in modern computations. Perhaps because they couldn't conceive of "nothing" as a number symbol, the Greeks and Romans of ancient times had no symbol to represent the empty column on the abacus. The symbol 0 came to us from the Hindu-Arabic system of numeration. This system revolutionized the mathematical world. Men were able to write any number, large or small, by using one, or a combination of ten, basic symbols. You know these ten symbols. They are: 0, 1, 2, 3, 4, 5, 6, 7, 8, and 9.

Like the Roman system of numeration, the Hindu-Arabic system was a decimal system, or system based on the quantity of ten. In fact, mathematicians say that the decimal system has a "base" of ten.

To understand what is meant by "a base of ten," and how with ten symbols we can write any number we want to, let's have another look at our abacus. When we pushed down the first four beads on the first wire, what was represented? When we pushed down four beads on the second, or tens wire, what number was represented?

The number we represented depended on two things: (1) *face value* (the number of beads); and (2) *place value* (the wire on which we pushed the beads down). Four beads on the ones wire represented 4, and four beads on the tens wire represented 40.

Writing numbers in the Hindu-Arabic system of numeration also depends on face value and place value. Each symbol in every number has both a face value and a place value.

Push four beads down on each of the five wires on your abacus. In the decimal system this can be written 44,444. It means:

$4 \times 10{,}000$ or	4 ten thousands	(ten thousands wire)
$4 \times 1{,}000$ or	4 thousands	(thousands wire)
4×100 or	4 hundreds	(hundreds wire)
4×10 or	4 tens	(tens wire)
4×1 or	4 ones	(ones wire)

$$40{,}000 + 4{,}000 + 400 + 40 + 4 = 44{,}444.$$

As the 4 moves one place (or wire) to the left, its face value remains the same, but its place value is ten times greater. Each column, or position of 4, represents a higher power of the base ten.

It is easy to see how zero, or the symbol 0, represents an empty column. It is a place holder, like the empty wire on the abacus.

We said that each column, or position of 4, represents a higher power of base ten. What is the power of a number?

In this multiplication example: $10 \times 10 = 100$, the numbers 10 and 10 are called *factors* of the number 100. If a factor appears twice as in $10 \times 10 = 100$, we can show this in another way: 10^2. Ten is now called the *base* and ^{2} is the *exponent*. An exponent is a power: 10^1 is only one power of 10, or simply 10; 10^2 is the second power of the base ten.

Let us look at some powers of base ten:

$$10^1 = 10$$
$$10^2 = 10 \times 10 = 100$$
$$10^3 = 10 \times 10 \times 10 = 1{,}000$$
$$10^4 = 10 \times 10 \times 10 \times 10 = 10{,}000.$$

You can see how 10^1 describes the tens column in the decimal system, 10^2 the hundreds column, 10^3 the thousands, and so on.

Looking again at the decimal number 44,444, we can see how the place value of 4 changes in different positions.

4	4	4	4	4
$4 \times 10{,}000$	$4 \times 1{,}000$	4×100	4×10	4×1
4×10^4	4×10^3	4×10^2	4×10^1	4×10^0

Place or position value, representing different powers of a base, is important to all numeration systems.

A REVIEW

To record our counting in the decimal number system, we found the following things to be essential:

1. A base (ten).
2. Number symbols (1, 2, 3, 4, 5, 6, 7, 8, and 9).
3. The symbol zero (0).
4. A symbol for the base ten, where place value is first introduced. When we move left to the second column we create our symbol for base ten by writing 10.

5. Position values of symbols (increasing powers of the base ten).

These essential features of the decimal system are mathematical concepts that man only arrived at after centuries of thought and application, and, through those centuries, mathematical concepts found their way to mechanical counting and measuring devices.

Chapter Two

THE BINARY AND OTHER NUMBER SYSTEMS

At the same time that our decimal system was being perfected, other number systems were also being developed. The Mayan Indians of Central America were improving a system that used 20 as a base, probably because they counted with fingers *and* toes. The Eskimos, in a much colder region, counted with a base of 5, probably because they counted on the fingers of only one hand.

About 4,000 years ago, the Chinese "discovered" a system based on 2, and then lost it. Later the system based on 2 was perfected by a seventeenth century European mathematician, Gottfried Leibnitz.

This system of numbers is called *the binary system* and to learn more about it let us go back to the abacus we built earlier. Take off eight beads on each wire, leaving us with two beads in each column. By doing this, we have converted our abacus from a decimal abacus to a binary abacus. Instead of representing fingers, where each column represents ten fingers, let us represent palms. Each column represents two palms. As soon as we have counted two palms we must exchange two beads in the ones column for one bead in the next column to the left.

Do you remember when we exchanged ten beads in the right-hand column of the decimal abacus for one in the next column to the left? The place value of a bead was multiplied by 10. On the binary abacus, exchanging two beads in the right-hand column for one in the next column to the left means that the value of a bead has been multiplied by 2.

If we represent ten on the decimal abacus we can write this as the symbol 10. It means that 1 bead is to be recorded in the tens column and 0 beads are to be recorded in the ones column.

Similarly, on the binary abacus, when there is 1 bead to be counted in the twos column and 0 beads to be counted in the ones column, we write the symbol 10 for two.

If we wanted to represent three on our abacus we should need to have one bead in the first column and one in the second; representing these beads in symbols we write 11. When we filled our second wire on the decimal abacus with ten tens, we exchanged them for one on the third wire, or column.

If we fill the second wire or column on the binary abacus with two beads we likewise must make an exchange, two beads for one on the third wire. The place value of the bead in this case has been multiplied by two again. It is now worth four in its position on the third wire.

Can you represent the number of players on a basketball team on your binary abacus?

The binary system is a way of representing any number with the symbols 1 and 0. The binary system gives a place value for 1 that doubles every time 1 moves one column to the left.

Try writing your age in the binary system.

We have said that the decimal system uses ten as a base. The binary system uses two as a base. An easy way to remember this relationship is to think how these numbers are written in each system:

10 = ten in decimal
10 = two in binary.

Because the binary system has:

1. A base (two)
2. The number symbol 1
3. A symbol for zero
4. A symbol (10) for the base when we move left to the second column
5. Position values of the symbol as the powers of the base increase, it fits our description of a number system. When a digit in base ten is shifted one place to the left, its value is multiplied by 10; when a digit in the binary system is shifted one place to the left, its value is multiplied by 2.

This binary number:

1	1	1	1	1
(Sixteens)	(Eights)	(Fours)	(Twos)	(Ones)

means:

$$
\begin{array}{cccccccccc}
2\times2\times2\times2 & & 2\times2\times2 & & 2\times2 & & 1\times2 & & 1\times1 & \\
16 & + & 8 & + & 4 & + & 2 & + & 1 & =31.
\end{array}
$$

The symbol 1 represents one, two, four, eight, or sixteen, depending on its place.

Try writing the numbers from 1 to 30 in the binary system. Remember: there are only two symbols and a place value. If you have five wires on your binary abacus, what is the highest number it can represent?

The binary system can be used for coding messages on punched paper tape. The binary number for each coded letter is recorded as a series of holes and spaces (or no holes); each hole represents the symbol 1, each space represents 0 (zero). For example: The letter D is the fourth number, and would be represented like this: 0 0 ● 0 0

Write out the alphabet as follows: A = 1, B = 10, C—11, etc., on a piece of paper. Use this key, and translate the message in the illustration.

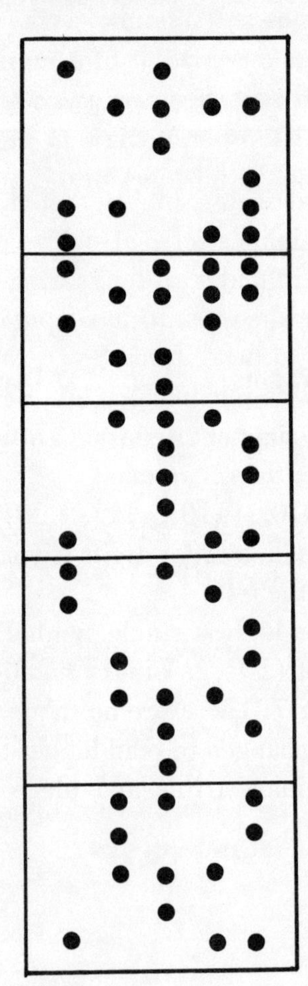

Note: Answers to problems begin on page 201

To increase your ability to "think binary," make up your own code and send this message: "Man is the measure of all things."

ON-OFF — ONE-ZERO

Here is a panel of six lights:
If each light, when lit, represents a power of base two, what binary number is being recorded on the panel? Can you tell what binary numbers these panels are representing?

With a little practice the binary system can be converted to the octal (base eight) system at sight. Very large numbers in the binary system make up long strings of 1 and 0 symbols so that people who work with computers often transpose data from binary to octal form. For example: A number like 10110111001 is put into triples. Begin with the low-order digits on the right and separate all the binary symbols into groups of three using commas:

010, 110, 111, 001

Annex a zero to the high-order digits if you need to complete your last triple to the left.

Seven (7) is the highest single symbol in base eight before we go to eight (10), in binary notation, 111 also represents the number 7. Therefore no triple in binary-to-octal conversion can be changed to read higher than seven (7).

Add up each binary triple and place the octal symbol below it.

This binary number:	010,	110,	111,	001
Reported as octal:	2	6	7	1
Means:	$2 \times 8^3 +$	$6 \times 8^2 +$	$7 \times 8^1 +$	1×8^0
	$2 \times 8 \times 8 \times 8$	$6 \times 8 \times 8$	7×8	1×1

The octal is "easy on the eyes," it is useful notation and is a convenient and customary notation in discussing numbers operated on by binary computers.

Can you write the proper binary triples for the octal word 1357602?

Can you convert the following binary numbers to octal?

1011101 11100001110011 1101111101111010101000

We said earlier that Eskimos have a number system based on five. If it is a true number system it must therefore fit our descriptions:

1. A base (five).
2. Number symbols (1, 2, 3, 4).
3. A symbol for zero.
4. A symbol (10) for the base when we move left to the second column.
5. Position values of the symbols as the powers of the base increase.

The number system based on five is called the *quinary system.* Let us convert our abacus to a quinary abacus by placing only five beads on a wire.

Do you know how the principles of exchange will apply now? As soon as you have five beads in any column you can exchange them for one bead in the next column to the left. Further, when a digit is shifted one place to the left its value is multiplied by five.

This quinary number means:

1	1	1	1	
One hundred and twenty-fives	Twenty-fives	Fives	Ones	
$1\times5\times5\times5$	$1\times5\times5$	1×5	1×1	
125 +	25 +	5 +	1	$=156$

This quinary number means:

3		4		2
Twenty-fives		Fives		Ones
$3\times5\times5$	+	4×5	+	$2\times1=97$

If there are five wires on your quinary abacus, what is the highest number it can represent?

PROBLEMS FOR YOU TO DO

1. Using the five points that describe a number system, explain the *ternary system* (the number system which is based on three) and solve:

$$\begin{array}{r}2\\+1\\\hline\end{array}\qquad\begin{array}{r}2102\\-\ 101\\\hline\end{array}\qquad\begin{array}{r}10221\\+11122\\\hline\end{array}\qquad\begin{array}{r}11201\\+\ 2100\\\hline\end{array}$$

2. Make a code in the octal system (the system based on eight) —

1 = A, 2 = B, 3 = C, 4 = D, 5 = E, 6 = F, 7 = G, 10 = H, etc., and send this message, using octal symbols: "Mathematics is a key to science."

Chapter Three

SPEED ARITHMETIC

WE ARE SURROUNDED by numbers. They are on our clocks, our buildings and homes, our money — just to mention a few places. Whether we are students or salesmen, doctors or engineers, shop workers or housewives, we must daily combine numbers with other numbers to obtain even more numbers. As we move up in school or ahead in our jobs, numbers gradually become almost as much a part of our language as English is. This is overwhelmingly true in business; indeed, it is reasonable to say that very few people become top-flight executives without being able to handle calculations and estimates with ease and speed.

Mathematicians have always been interested in learning new properties of numbers. Many of today's business people take advantage of those properties of numbers that enable them to make fast estimates with a minimum of paper and pencil work.

Some properties of numbers can only apply to the specific number under consideration, while some are so general that they can be applied to all numbers in a given process. By process we mean one of the four basic arithmetic operations — addition, multiplication, subtraction, and division.

This chapter is concerned primarily with properties of numbers or properties of an arithmetical process that are general enough to be quickly applied to develop speed in computations. Scientists and engineers use powers, roots, and logarithms, but these make up too small a part of business and personal arithmetic to be included in this section. Speed arithmetic has one invaluable function in business and personal use — rapid, time-saving *estimation.* To explore these properties, let us proceed with one process at a time.

Most of our computations are done in the operation of *addition.*

ADDITION

In reading the last sentence, you probably grouped words or even phrases in a glance. Much the same thing can be done in grouping numbers. Add this column of digits, for example.

$$\begin{array}{c} 3 \\ 8 \\ 2 \\ \underline{9} \end{array}$$

Many of us will interrupt the grouping of numbers by saying "and" between numbers. Instead of saying 3 and 8 are 11 and 2 are 13 and 9 are 22, it is faster and less confusing to think, "11, 13, 22."

Just as you have developed a skill for the rapid recognition of words, so you can develop a sense of numbers.

Do not call out each new digit. Think only of the answers. When you read the word "he" you do not say an *h* and an *e* make a "he." With a little practice you should be able to combine numbers just as easily as you combine letters.

4	7	3	2
9	3	8	5
8	5	9	1
2	8	6	3
3	4	7	4

As with letters, we also read numbers from left to right; yet (except for division), when we perform *operations* on numbers, we work from right to left. Since the highest-order digits, or numbers, to the left are usually the most important, let us try a few problems adding from left to right.

Suppose you are a tire salesman and have just completed several orders. Your boss is speaking to you long distance by telephone to inquire about your day's work. He is in a hurry and only wants a quick estimate.

$308.76
421.92
507.04
316.13

All of us, including your boss, read from left to right, and certainly the numbers on the left are the most important to him.

You note that the figures in the tens and units columns (left of the decimal point) are less than 100. Add the digits in the hundreds column, then say 1500. Now, run your eye up the tens and units columns.

Use the combining (or grouping) technique and say (without using the word "and") 1523, 1544, 1552; then add 2 more dollars, because the first column to the right of the decimal point contains nearly two dollars. An estimate to the nearest dollar was probably all your boss needed and you speeded up this answer to him by working from left to right.

Add the column of figures below using this new technique. It should only take 8 to 10 seconds. (Note that the sum of digits in the tens and units columns is less than 100.) Be sure to "group" numbers and estimate to the nearest dollar.

```
$218.00
 701.43
 623.09
 309.15
-------
```

If you had to combine figures in the tens and units columns that were over 100, you would first write down the answer for your highest-order digit (1800) then proceed to group or combine the units and tens columns on the next line. Thus, in the following problem:

```
$ 391
  420
  602
  536
-----
 1800
 (1)49
-----
 1949
```

Write down, combine, and write the total 1949.

The circled figure is, of course, a "carry" into the hundreds column.

It is sometimes a good technique, when mentally adding numbers that end in 6, 7, 8, or 9, to increase the units digit to 10, add the 10, then subtract from the answer the number by which the original number was increased.

Thus, if you are combining 45 and 29, think 45 and *30* as 75, then subtract 1 to get 74. Combining 64 and 97, think 64 and 100 less 3, or 161.

Practice this technique with these numbers:

75	63	21	77
98	78	19	58
	29	37	99
		14	12
			30

Bookkeepers and cashiers often run into very long columns of figures and many times their computations are interrupted by physical or mental distractions such as a customer's coming into the office or a phone call. One practical way of dealing with this problem and avoiding errors is to create subtotals. Here is an illustration:

138		
09		
214		
172		
63		
317	596	subtotals
96		
41		
592		
986		
08	2032	
76		
921		
632		
95		
	1732	

You can see that the longer column may be broken down into subtotals by drawing a line under every five numbers.

Another equally exasperating job is to total shorter columns of larger numbers. One technique that provides an easy check of any column, without doing the whole problem over, is putting the "carry" digit on its own line.

```
                  3498762
                  8941604
                  1786432
                  6538149
                  -------
                  8543837
carry digits →   12221110 ← 0 or no carry digits in
                 --------     the units column
                 20764947
```

Can you see why it is easy to check each individual column? The carry does not become part of any column. Instead, it becomes a number that is computed with the answer when all the columns have been tallied. Don't forget to put each carry down in the next column to the left.

Add the numbers below using the technique of the extra line. (Be sure to place the digit used as a carry into the column containing the next highest order of digits.)

```
764321          4378962
980768          5130961
673546          7324560
140513          8701329
------          -------
```

Another usual device forms an "angle" with the answer.

```
 387
 419
 276
 567
----
  29
 220
1400
----
1649
```

Care must be taken to make sure that each sum is in the right place (use 0 as a place holder if necessary at first): unit digits in the units column, the last digit from the tens column total in the tens column, the last digit of the hundreds column in the hundreds column, and so on.

Try these using this angular method with these numbers:

```
496     637     709
273     867     963
409     129     143
972     243     277
---     ---     ---
```

Checking these long columns of figures is often a tedious job. The usual procedure is to add down if you've added up first or to add up if you've first added down.

By trying the following fresh approach to the problem, you will not only keep your mind alert but you will be using a rapid and near-perfect process. This process relies upon the *digit sum.* A digit sum is simply the sum of all of the digits in a given number. For example the digit sum of 15 is $1 + 5$ or simply 6. The digit sum of 223 is $2 + 2 + 3 = 7$.

Finding the digit sum of 875 becomes a matter of continuous reduction to one number by adding two numbers at a time from left to right. Thus, $8 + 7 = 15$. Reduce 15 to $1 + 5 = 6$. Add this to 5 (the ones digit in 875), $6 + 5 = 11$, reduce this to $1 + 1 = 2$. The digit sum of 875 is 2.

Remember: always reduce to one digit whenever the sum goes over 9. Ten (10), of course, is simply $1 + 0 = 1$.

You must always reduce to one digit at the end.

We can speed up the process of finding the digit sum by *casting out 9's*. In 59, $5 + 9 = 14$ and $1 + 4 = 5$. The 9 does not change the digit sum. Try 29, 39, 49, or 1,999, 299, 39,999, etc., just to be sure.

When adding digit sums, cast out any 9's you see or any combination of digits that add up to 9. For example:

236	981
541	6372

Cast out the 0's also, except when the final or end result is a 0.

Now to check some addition problems with this technique.

Problem	*Digit Sums*
132	6
493	7
271	1
896	14

The digit sum of the answer is $8 + 6 = 14 = 1 + 4 = 5$. The sum of digit sums is also 14 which reduces to $1 + 4 = 5$. Since the digit sums check, 896 can be considered as the correct answer.

Since the chance of making an error in checking by digit

sums is something like once in a century, it is a very practical way to check problems in addition.

Try working these problems, adding by grouping and checking by digit sums:

27	76
18	21
53	93
12	62
41	50

Work these problems by the angular method and check by digit sums:

492	630
376	798
981	541
	226

Now try this problem by using a separate line for the carry digits and check by digit sums:

379864
425731
862406
516249

One area in speed arithmetic that has applications in computers and Boolean algebra is the use of *complements.* By definition, a complement simply means a *complete set.*

We can select any group of numbers as a complete set. Because we are working in the decimal system, we will say that 10 makes a complete set of numbers. Do you remember when we added numbers that ended in 6, 7, 8, and 9? We increased the unit's digit to 10, added the 10, then subtracted from the answer the number by which the original number had been increased. We combined 45 and 29. We changed 29 to 30 to get 75, then subtracted 1 to get 74. That 1 was the complement of 9. Together they made a complete set of 10.

The tens complement is merely the digit that together with the digit you already have adds up to 10. In other words, two digits whose sum is 10 are called tens complements of each other.

The tens complement of 6 is 4 $(6 + 4 = 10)$.
The tens complement of 7 is 3 $(7 + 3 = 10)$.
The tens complement of 8 is 2 $(8 + 2 = 10)$.

And, of course, the tens complement of 9 is 1.

Do you know the tens complement of 5? Of course, it is 5.

In speed addition using the complements, we only use the tens complements of numbers larger than 5. That is, we only use the tens complements of 6, 7, 8, and 9 — *and*, we always use the tens complement of the larger digit, never the smaller.

A problem like $4 + 9$ can also be stated as $4 + (10 - 1)$.

1. $4 + 9$
2. $4 + (10 - 1)$
3. $4 + 10 - 1$
4. $4 - 1 + 10$
5. $3 + 10$
6. 13 is always the answer.

Or:

Substitute 4 + 10 + (−1) for step 3.
Substitute 4 + (−1) + 10 for step 4.

Adding by complements is really a matter of taking advantage of a basic mathematical principle to attain speed in computations.

To add 4 + 9 we *subtract* the complement of the larger digit 9 from the smaller digit 4. Then add a 10.

```
  4
 −1 — The tens complement of 9.
 ---
  3
+10
 ---
 13
```

A little practice will make this easy.

```
  8        8        7        7
 +9       +3       +9       +5
 --       --       --       --
```

Instead of adding the 10's, we can simply note this by placing a dot whenever you use a complement or add up 10. When you write your total, add up the total number of dots. Two dots = 2, three dots = 3, etc., and place the answer in the *next* column to the left.

Reminder: Work from left to right.

```
  3 5
  2.5
 .8 4
 ----
  3 4
 11
 ----
 14 4
```

Left hand column: 3 + 2 is 5. The tens complement of 8 is 2; therefore, 5 − 2 is 3. Put a dot next to the 8 because we have used a complement. Put a 3 under the line in the column.
Right hand column: 5 + 5 is 10. Note this by placing a dot next to the second 5. Add the 4 and place it under the line in the units column.

Now, take the dot from the tens column and add it as 1 into the hundreds column. Then take the dot in the units column and add 1 in the tens columns, just as we moved the carry digit into the next highest column. (The dot is the symbol for a carry.)

You should now be ready to try these.

```
39      376      987      8762
16      842      214      3459
52      165      750      2175
--      ---      346      6304
                 ---      1987
                          ----
```

To stay alert, it is a good procedure to perform addition by one speed technique and to check results by another.

SUBTRACTION

Probably the least complex of the four basic arithmetic processes is subtraction. Even so, complements can be used to speed up subtraction estimates that are performed from left to right. The technique of adding digit sums can be used to check the answers.

Subtraction, of course, is the reverse of addition, and the complement technique works in reverse.

Earlier, we added $8 + 9$ by subtracting the tens complement of 9 and noting a 10 to get 17. To subtract 8 from 17 by using the tens complement, *add* the tens complement of the subtrahend to the minuend. When you use the complement in subtraction you must cancel out the 10. This procedure is the reverse of addition by complements.

Remember: In addition, you *subtract* the tens complement and *add 10* by placing a dot next to the digit you have processed. In subtraction, you *add* the tens complement and *cancel* a 10.

Minuend	$\not{1}7$	(canceling out the 10)
Subtrahend	$\underline{8}$	
Difference	9	

The tens complement of 8 is 2. Add $2 + 7 = 9$ and cancel the 1 in the tens column.

If the minuend is larger than the subtrahend, subtract in the conventional way.

$$\begin{array}{r} 8 \\ \underline{-2} \\ 6 \end{array}$$

When the subtrahend is larger than the minuend, use the tens complement.

In subtraction, we use the tens complement with *all* of the digits, including those digits which are less than 5.

The tens complement of 4 is 6.
The tens complement of 3 is 7.
The tens complement of 2 is 8.
The tens complement of 1 is 9.

Do you remember canceling out the 10 when we subtracted 8 from 17?

In addition by complements, we used the dot to note that a 1 was to be added into the next column to the left. In subtraction, the diagonal line will cancel out only the face value of a 1. For example, ~~1~~0 becomes 0, ~~4~~0 is 30, ~~2~~10 is 110. This line through a digit means that it is to be made one smaller than it was.

Now for a practical application. Again let us suppose that you are that same tire salesman who received a long-distance call from his boss. Your sales total for that day was $1,553.85, and now your boss asks how it compares with your sales for the same day last month. A quick check through your sales record shows that business on that day was $1,372.56. Since the highest-order digits are usually the most important to any boss, begin subtracting from the left by complements. Watch this answer carefully as it develops:

```
$1553.85
 1372.56
--------
 0281.39
```
(with diagonal lines through the 2 and the 3 of the answer)

1 − 1 is 0, in 5 − 3 the subtrahend is smaller than the minuend, so simply put down 2. Now look at 5 − 7. The subtrahend is larger than the minuend; therefore, add the tens complement of 7 to 5. That is 3 + 5 = 8. Because we have used the complement in this case, draw a diagonal line through the 2 which is found in the difference (or answer) in the next column to the left. To continue, 3 − 2 is 1. On the other side of the decimal point, 8 − 5 is 3. Lastly, add the tens complement of 6 to 5; that is, 4 + 5 =

9 and, because we used the complement, mark the diagonal line through the digit in the next column to the left (on the difference or answer line).

Reduce by 1 the digits which have been slashed ($0~~2~~81.~~3~~9) and your answer to your boss reads $181.29.

Of course, this is a very simple problem, but suppose a great deal more money was involved and your boss wanted just as rapid an estimate. See if you can do the following problems in less than 10 seconds each, starting from the left and rounding off the answer to the nearest one hundred dollars.

$477,365.00
−96,472.00
____

$7,396,421.00
−6,418,212.00
____

$9,417,919.00
−4,520,820.00
____

Now we will check our answers by using digit sums. Before going on to this you might review the paragraphs on digit sums.

In order to illustrate this technique, we will not stop at the nearest hundred dollars, but will do the entire problem.

477,365	5
−96,472	−1
~~4~~8~~1~~,~~9~~93	
380,893	4

These are two ways to proceed. In the above example, you can subtract the digit sums as shown and this answer should equal the digit sum of the difference (or answer).

Suppose the digit sum of the subtrahend was larger than the digit sum of the minuend. Look at the second problem.

```
  7,396,421     5
 −6,418,212     6
 ----------    ---
  1,988,219
    978,209     8
```

(In the printed working, the 1 and 9 of 1,988,219 and its 1 in 219 are struck through.)

You must proceed in an alternate fashion to check this problem. Do you remember when you checked subtraction by the conventional method? You added the difference to the subtrahend to get the minuend. Follow the same procedure above with the digit sums. (Remember to reduce your answer to one digit: 8 + 6 is 14; reduce this to 1 + 4 = 5 and your answer checks. Now subtract and check the last problem on your own. Remember that there are two possible procedures in checking subtraction by digit sums. Be sure you select the correct one for this problem.

```
  9,417,919
  4,520,820
 ----------
```

MULTIPLICATION

Multiplication is the second most used operation in business and personal arithmetic. It might be helpful to remember two concepts in multiplication:

1. Think of the process as a matter of repeated additions;

thus, 3×5 is three fives or

$$\begin{array}{r} 5 \\ 5 \\ 5 \\ \hline 15 \end{array}$$

2. Keep the multiplier smaller than the multiplicand even if it means commuting them; thus, $\begin{array}{r} 3 \\ \times 41 \\ \hline \end{array}$ should be changed to read $\begin{array}{r} 41. \\ \times 3 \\ \hline \end{array}$

Some Special Short Cuts

The digit 5 is a very interesting multiplier. If we had this problem:

$$\begin{array}{lr} \text{Multiplicand} & 68 \\ \text{Multiplier} & \times\ 5 \\ \hline & 340 \end{array}$$

most of us would probably approach it in the conventional fashion, multiplying the 8, putting down an 0, carrying 4, multiplying the 6 in the multiplicand, and adding 4 to the product. Actually, the product could have been calculated without pencil and paper by multiplying by 10, $(68 \times 10 = 680)$ and mentally dividing the product by 2 (because 5 is half of 10): $2\overline{)680} = 340$.

Because of its relationship to 10, the digit 9 also has useful properties. If we have the problem $\begin{array}{r} 7842, \\ \times\ \ \ 9 \\ \hline \end{array}$ we can think of 9 as being the equivalent of $10 - 1$, and our problem can be reduced to a simple exercise in subtraction.

7842 × 10	is	78420
7842 × 1	is	− 7842
7842 × 9	is	70578

Do you see a short cut in the following problem?

$$\begin{array}{r} 163 \\ \times\ 99 \\ \hline \end{array}$$

The trick lies in 99's proximity to 100. Can you work it out?

One often-used method of speed multiplication is the *break-down method.* Like all other short cuts in arithmetic, the effectiveness of this method is dependent on the manner of break-down.

The break-down method is possible when the multiplier can be *factored* or broken down into two other multipliers. For example, the number 16 might be broken down into the factors of 4 and 4 (4 × 4 is 16) or the factors of 8 and 2 (8 × 2 = 16). If we use the factors 8 and 2, the following examples will illustrate the time-saving value of the break-down method.

Conventional	*Break-down*
736	736
× 16	× 8
4416	5888
7360	× 2
11776	11776

The break-down method can also be used as a check on the conventional process.

Try these problems, using the break-down method.

$$\begin{array}{r} 892 \\ \times\ 24 \\ \hline \end{array} \qquad \begin{array}{r} 6891 \\ \times\ \ 35 \\ \hline \end{array}$$

Another break-down method takes advantage of a basic mathematical principle to get rapid answers. This break-down method regards the *multiplicand* as a sum of two numbers. In this problem, $\begin{array}{r} 35 \\ \times\ 3 \\ \hline \end{array}$ can be computed mentally (working from left to right) as $(30 \times 3) + (5 \times 3)$ or $90 + 15 = 105$.

In the process of multiplication, many techniques can be used to obtain speed in the computation. In fact, there is a short cut for almost every multiplication problem. Most of these, however, are concerned with the properties of individual numbers or digits and have no place in practical applications of speed arithmetic.

Generally, problems in which the multiplier is a single digit can be computed very easily and rapidly from left to right.

Let's take an example apart to see why this works.

$$\begin{array}{r} 78 \\ \times\ 3 \\ \hline 24 \\ \text{(three 70's)} \rightarrow 210 \\ \hline 234 \end{array} = \begin{array}{r} 70 \\ \times\ 3 \\ \hline 210 \end{array} \text{ plus } \begin{array}{r} 8 \\ \times 3 \\ \hline 24 \end{array} = 234.$$

Look at the answer, 234 —

The highest-order digit, 2, is the hundreds digit of 70×3.

The next highest order, 3, is the sum of the two tens digits, $1 + 2$, and the lowest-order digit, 4, is the units digit of 8×3.

Try another —

	36	
	× 7	Put this product down
Put this product down	42	← second
first →	210	
	252	

Try these on your own.

$$\begin{array}{r} 82 \\ \times\ 9 \\ \hline \end{array} \qquad \begin{array}{r} 47 \\ \times\ 3 \\ \hline \end{array} \qquad \begin{array}{r} 26 \\ \times\ 7 \\ \hline \end{array}$$

Now, let's try another multiplication problem, writing down only the final answer, or sum, of the products.

$$\begin{array}{r} 82 \\ \times\ 7 \\ \hline 574 \end{array}$$

The first digit, 5, of the product 8×7 will be in the hundreds column of your answer. Write in the 5.

Now, only *think* the second digit of the product 8×7. It will be in the tens column. Do not write, but *remember* the 6. Next, the first digit of the product of 7×2 is in the tens column. Add this 1 to the 6 you remembered and write a 7 in the tens column. Mentally, multiply 7×2 again and write down the units digit, 4.

Try these on your own.

$$\begin{array}{r} 53 \\ \times\ 6 \\ \hline \end{array} \qquad \begin{array}{r} 89 \\ \times\ 2 \\ \hline \end{array} \qquad \begin{array}{r} 522 \\ \times\ 6 \\ \hline \end{array}$$

How did you make out?

Perhaps this is an unusual way to develop a product, but take your time and think about this operation for a moment.

At the second step you had to remember the tens digit. You would have had to do this by the traditional method anyhow. The advantage of this left-to-right procedure lies in the fact that you are processing the important numbers first. What does this mean in a practical application?

Let us go back to the salesman who got the phone call from his boss. When we left him he reported $1,553.85 as the day's totals. Suppose his boss wanted to make a fast estimate of his commission at 8 per cent. Can you compute this to the nearest dollar in five seconds? (Don't forget to move the decimal point in your answer two places to the left because 8 per cent should read as .08.) A commission of $124.00 is not bad.

Let us examine the steps processed mentally by the salesman's boss. To see them clearly, we will write them out.

$$\begin{array}{r} \$1553.85 \\ .08 \\ \hline 40 \\ 64 \\ 24 \\ 40 \\ 40 \\ 08 \\ \hline \$124.2080 \end{array}$$

Because we have six digits in the multiplicand, let us start six lines down. Although the answer to the first product, 8 × 1, is a single digit, it represents 8 thousand dollars and must remain in the thousands dollar column. It must also be added to the carry digit of the second step (8 × 5). (Sometimes 0 may be used as a place holder on the left when the next highest column is empty.)

Of course, you noticed that the decimal point was moved over two places to the left, but you must also have noticed that this answer is not complete. There must be a carry from the original ones dollar column to the tens dollar column. We have circled the 2 in the fourth column from the left. Do you remember when we added the dots in addition by complements? We increased by 1 the face value of the next column to the left.

In speed multiplication, by drawing a circle around a digit we increase its face value by 1. Thus, the 2 is now changed to 3 and the answer reads $124.3080. Of course, the boss didn't need the 3 to compute to the nearest dollar, but he may have needed it when he called other salesmen. Suppose he had to compute their totals at 8 per cent. Suppose you were the boss and had to complete these problems in five seconds each.

Write only the final answers, making sure to circle a digit when it will be affected by a 1 carry.

Salesman B — $467.95 × 8%
Salesman C — $288.07 × 8%

Do you know how the boss might prove his answers in the last three percentage problems?

He might add up the total sales of tire salesmen A, B, and C, then multiply by .08. This product should equal the total amount of the three individual commissions that he computed when talking to A, B, and C over the phone.

Another Short Cut

Suppose every customer that bought four tires received a 20 per cent discount. The traditional method of computation would be as follows:

4 tires	\$80.00		\$80.00
less 20%	.20	less discount	16.00
	\$16.00		\$64.00

The conventional way is unnecessarily long. It takes two processes to get the same results that can be gotten in one multiplication problem. This one operation recognizes the discount of 20 per cent as creating a selling price which is 80 per cent of the original price. The tire discount could have been processed in this manner:

$$\begin{array}{r} \$80.00 \\ \times .80 \\ \hline \$64.00 \end{array}$$

Eighty per cent, of course, is the *hundreds* complement of 20 per cent. Can you do these problems in one process?

1. A \$75.00 suit is discounted 10 per cent. What is its selling price?

2. A \$6.70 carton of soap is discounted 20 per cent. What is its selling price?

In problem 2 you can use complements to help you add in step 2.

$$\begin{array}{r} 06.70 \\ .80 \\ \hline \end{array}$$

Step one — 6 × 8 is in the 40's; write down 4 in the column on the left.

Step two — 6 × 8 ends in 8, the digit we must remember. Since 7 × 8 is in the 50's, instead of adding 8 + 5 = 13, subtract the complement of 8 (which is 2) from 5. Write down a three in the next column and circle the digit in the next column to the left to indicate a 1 carry.

Step three — 7 × 8 ends in 6. Be sure the decimal point is in the correct place.

Do two more problems to help these processes become a habit before you go on to two- and three-digit multipliers.

$$\begin{array}{r} 879 \\ \times \ \ 7 \\ \hline \end{array} \qquad\qquad \begin{array}{r} 394 \\ \times \ \ 8 \\ \hline \end{array}$$

In two-digit multipliers, begin the multiplication with the digit on the left and proceed as before. When you write the product for the next multiplier (the one on the right), you must be sure to begin your second product one place to the right, as in the following example:

	64	
	×46	Place
Product using ten's-digit multiplier —	2560	← holder
Product using unit's-digit multiplier —	384	
	2944	

The place holder, 0, indicates that you are, in effect, multiplying by 40. We could have spelled it out thus: $(40 \times 64) + (6 \times 64)$.

The product using the ten's-digit multiplier is really forty 64's.

The product using the unit's-digit multiplier is really six 64's.

Using three- and four-digit multipliers, proceed as with two-digit multipliers. Begin with the farthest digit to the left and place products for each succeeding multiplier one place value to the right.

The strongest feature of the left-to-right multiplicand is that it makes quick *estimates* possible. This cannot be done by conventional means. By using speed multiplication, you can get a two-digit estimate in seconds, and a three-digit estimate while the man with the slide rule is still getting it on the desk.

$$\begin{array}{r} 359 \\ \times 274 \\ \hline \end{array} \qquad \begin{array}{r} 678 \\ \times 213 \\ \hline \end{array} \qquad \begin{array}{r} \$392.31 \\ \times 43.52 \\ \hline \end{array}$$

For these first two problems, make a two-digit estimate; for the third, make a three-digit estimate.

DIVISION

Perhaps the least commonly used process is division. It is multiplication in reverse and may be considered as a process of repeated subtractions. In the operation of division, we have all been taught to work from left to right. Division is very clearly a process of continuous estimation.

Before taking up any short cuts, let us first look at a very modern approach to teaching division.

In the following multiplication problem 24 × 42, the answer is 1008. Let us use this as a dividend and 24 as a divisor. Our quotient should be 42.

```
       42   |
24 ) 1008   |
      960   | 40
      ---   |
       48   |
       48   |  2
      ---   |---
            | 42
```

Our first estimate is of how many 24's will go into 1008, and our best answer is that forty 24's will go into 1008. Draw a line alongside the problem to separate this new grouping of numbers and write down 40 on the same line as your subtrahend, 960.

After you have completed the first subtraction, make your second estimate of how many 24's will go into 48. Of course it is 2. Add 40 + 2 as the quotient.

What has been shown here is that in the process of estimating the quotient we did not confuse a 4 with a 40.

Try 36) 16668, taking care not to confuse the place value of your continuous estimates. Work the following problems by using the techniques you have learned in this chapter:

Multiply from left to right.

Subtract from left to right.

Make correct place value estimates.

345) 9970   892) 327,464

Now, to use a short-cut method of speed division, you will need to hold some numbers in your memory much as a computer does when it performs some arithmetic operations.

Perhaps the most useful way that division can be speeded up with less paper and pencil work is by the so-called *short continental method.*

Divide: $36\overline{)16668}$.

Let us see how this answer develops. The step-by-step procedure for solving this problem by the short continental method is as follows:

The divisor, 36, is contained in 166 four times. Write a 4 in the quotient. Multiply 4 × 36 to get 144. Deduct 144 mentally from 166 and write down the difference, 22. Bring down the next digit from the dividend — 226 should now appear under the dividend.

$$\begin{array}{r} 4 \\ 36\overline{)16668} \\ 226 \end{array}$$

Try 6 as the next digit in the quotient and proceed as before: 6 × 36 is 216. Mentally subtract 216 from 226, write in 10 under 26 and bring down the 8.

$$\begin{array}{r} 463 \\ 36\overline{)16668} \\ 226 \\ 108 \end{array}$$

We can quickly see that 3 × 36 is 108. Put the 3 in the quotient to complete your answer.

Take advantage of the short continental method in the problems that follow. One of them contains a remainder. Simply put this remainder into your answer as you do in the traditional method.

$105\overline{)8820}$ $\qquad\qquad$ $59\overline{)6985}$

The process of division, like multiplication, has other properties that should be taken advantage of. Do you remember when we broke down multipliers into separate factors? In division the same process can be applied to divisors.

In the following problem, $48\overline{)6336}$, the divisor, 48, can be factored into 6 × 8; thus $\frac{6336}{6\times8}$. Can you solve this without pencil and paper?

Step 1 — 6336 (mentally) divided by 6 is 1056.

Step 2 — The quotient becomes the new dividend; 1056 divided by the remaining divisor, 8, is 132.

Try these first by breaking down the divisor into factors:

$32\overline{)2428}$ $\qquad\qquad$ $24\overline{)4008}$

Remainders

In division, the quotient often contains a remainder, or that part of the answer which the divisor cannot equally divide.

In the problem $56\overline{)364}$, two factors of 56 are 7 and 8. If you began dividing by 7, the answer was 52. If you took the other factor first, dividing 364 by 8 gave $45\frac{1}{2}$. This fraction should be converted to its decimal equivalent and the process continued (45.5 divided by 7 is 6.5).

Try this problem: $36\overline{)386}$

Using the factors 6 × 6, convert the first remainder to a decimal and continue. Be sure to place the decimal point in the correct position in your answer.

The terms *reduce to* and *reduce by* are often confused in problems that involve the operation of division.

To reduce *by* one fourth means to subtract one fourth. For example, to reduce the air speed of 360 miles per hour by ¼ means to divide 4 into 360 and subtract this quotient from 360: $\frac{360}{4} = 90$; then $360 - 90 = 270$. The air speed is now 270 miles per hour.

If the instruction was to reduce air speed *to* one fourth of 360, the problem would simply be $\frac{360}{4}$, or 90.

Probably the most important thing is not the arithmetic processes themselves. Rather it is the way we think. When we are presented with problems in science, school, or business, we must have a clear picture of how we are going to deal with them.

Let us have a look at a harbor engineer who is unable to sleep because of a problem he began to think about right after he retired for the night. The room was dark, pencil and paper were in another room, and he was not inclined to turn on the light. As for the problem, the engineer knew that salt water was infiltrating a small fresh-water tributary which emptied into a certain harbor. He also knew that the rate of this infiltration was eight hundred gallons a day. To study the action of the salt water upon the fresh water he had decided to build a hydrodynamic model. His specific concern was how much flow could be studied in one hour's observation in a laboratory. Normally the problem would be one of the division of $24\overline{)800}$, but the harbor engineer still had no intention of getting out of bed for a pencil and paper. He took advantage of the relationship of 2 to each of the numbers, 24 and 800. He kept mentally breaking down each number by half until he computed the salt water flow per hour as follows: 800 divided by 24 equals 400 divided by 12 equals 200, divided by 6 equals 100, divided by 3. At this point it was simple to determine that $33\frac{1}{3}$ gallons of salt water were to be used per hour in his hydrodynamic model.

Knowing how to use our sense of numbers is an art. The secret of mastering this art is the same as that of mastering a musical instrument. The secret is *practice.*

Numbers have properties that can be taken advantage of. Sometimes quick mental estimates make demands on us. Much like the memory units on a computer, we hold a number or two in our minds while working out a specific part of the problem.

Below are some problems that cover all of the techniques presented in this chapter. Just to remind you, by way of a summary, here are —

Digit sums
Casting out 9's
Work from left to right
Use of complements
Grouping numbers
Angular addition
Break-down methods

PROBLEMS

1. 5,785 fish were caught every day by 793 licensed fishermen. How many did each catch in a five-day week? How many fish were caught in nine days?

2. You don't need pencil and paper for this one: 400 baseball umpires took an eye test and only 35 had 20/20 vision. How many did not?

3. 736,984 fidgits were produced last year. This year's production has only reached 708,795. The company president telephones the factory manager breathlessly, "Quick, what's the percentage decrease in fidgits?" Give him an estimate to the nearest hundred before he decides to call a stockholders' meeting.

Chapter Four

SETS AND CIRCUITS

A Simple Computer and Boolean Algebra

Would it be possible for us to design a computer that is capable of making some simple decisions? To find out, first examine the two circuits, *A* and *B*, in the accompanying diagram.

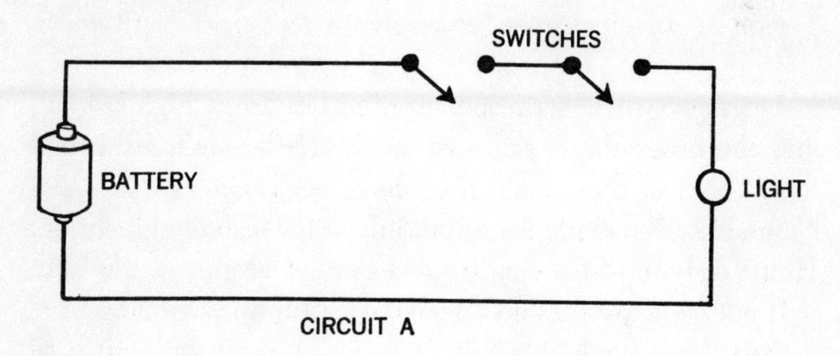

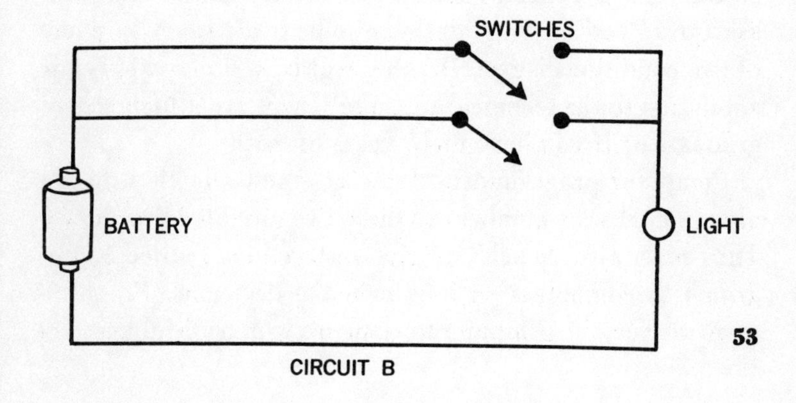

Because we want these circuits to make decisions for us, we can let each switch represent a condition instead of a binary number. If the conditions are met, the switch will be closed and the light will go on, making a "yes" decision.

If the conditions are not met, the switches will not be closed and the light will not go on. The circuit thereby gives a "no" decision.

Do you see how circuit A can handle the following situation?

> IF you are a high school graduate *and* IF you have taken three years of math, you may apply for admission to an electronics course in a technical institute.

Let one switch represent graduation from high school, and the other three years of math. If the light is turned "on," both of these conditions have been met. A "yes" decision has been made for admission to the technical institute. If one or both of the conditions have not been met, the light will not go on and a "no" decision will have been made.

Now let us look at circuit B. It is a circuit that will turn on the light if *either* of the switches is closed. We can now ask for a "yes" or "no" decision to be made when only *one* of two conditions is met. In other words, you may apply for admission to the technical institute if you are a high school graduate *or* if you have three years of math.

Computer programmers, logicians, and scientists do not always deal with numbers as these two circuits have shown. They must also "teach" or give instructions (called a program) to computers on how to make decisions. Programmers instruct the computer to come up with truthful answers about propositions that are concerned with the subject matter of science or mathematics.

There is a branch of mathematics called Boolean algebra that helps computer programmers, scientists, and others to do this work. Actually, it does not deal with numbers only but with *sets* or *classes* of objects. It is named for George Boole, a British logician, who constructed this algebra of logic. Certain operations are performed on these sets of objects that are similar to the operations of arithmetic on numbers.

To learn more about this kind of algebra, let us first review the following ground rules of arithmetic.

The Commutative Law of Addition: Write the sum of two numbers. Then write the sum by interchanging these two numbers. For example: In $4 + 2 = 2 + 4$, the sums are equal. In algebraic form we may also state: $X + Y = Y + X$.

The Commutative Law of Multiplication is similar to the Commutative Law of Addition. For example: $3 \times 2 = 2 \times 3$ or $XY = YX$. (In algebra we leave out the times sign ($\times$) to avoid confusing it with the letter X.)

The Associative Law of Addition states that when we add three numbers the sum will be the same whether we add the middle number to the first or third number.

Expressed:

$$\begin{array}{r} 3 \\ 4 \\ +\,9 \\ \hline \end{array} \quad \text{is the same as} \quad \begin{array}{r} 9 \\ 4 \\ +\,3 \\ \hline \end{array}$$

or $$3 + (4 + 9) = (3 + 4) + 9.$$

Expressed in algebraic
terms: $X + (Y + Z) = (X + Y) + Z.$
The parentheses indicate the first sum to be taken.

The Associative Law of Multiplication likewise states that:

$$(3 \times 4) \times 9 = 3 \times (4 \times 9)$$

or

$$(XY)Z = X(YZ).$$

The Distributive Law can be described as follows:

$$5(3 + 4) = (5 \times 3) + (5 \times 4) = 35$$

or

$$X(Y + Z) = XY + XZ.$$

Do you see that multiplication is distributive with respect to addition? Addition is *not* distributive with respect to multiplication. The multiplier can be distributed among the terms it multiplies, but addition and multiplication cannot change places, thus:

$$(5 + 3) \times (5 + 4) = 72$$

or

$$(X + Y)\,(X + Z).$$

The Commutative, Associative and Distributive Laws describe the operations performed in a number system. Both the laws and the number system are useful because of their dependability in these operations of addition and multiplication.

These laws on the operations of addition and multiplication are applicable to operations in Boolean algebra. However, before we can do any operations in Boolean algebra, you should remember that Boolean algebra does not deal with numbers as we usually think of them. Boolean algebra deals with *sets* or classes of objects. This may sound rather vague and mysterious at first, and you may wonder how we can perform addition and multiplication on sets or classes of objects. Let us find out.

Imagine for a moment that your mother is setting the table for dinner. First she puts out all the knives, forks, and spoons. These objects are classed, or described generally, as the "silverware." Cups, saucers, soup bowls, and plates are classed as "dishes." "Glasses" for water or milk can also be regarded as a set of objects. All of these objects can roughly be described or classed as a *universe* of all the objects needed on our dinner table.

To make our operations simpler, let us refer to these sets of objects by symbols:

$\triangle$ will represent silverware.

$\bigcirc$ will represent dishes.

$\square$ will represent glasses.

We can describe the universe, or the full table, as 1, sometimes called U. The empty table, or a class we will call the empty set, will be termed 0. If the universe, or 1, contains $\triangle$, $\bigcirc$, and $\square$, we can say $1 = \triangle$, $\bigcirc$, and $\square$. All other sets are subsets of the universe set. For example, it is possible to have only △ and ○ in a subset, or ○ and □.

Here is a list of all the sets of △, ○, and □.

Each subset will be given a letter name so that we may refer to it very easily.

UNIVERSE

1 = △ ○ □

SUBSETS

A = △ ○
B = △ □
C = ○ □
D = △
E = ○
F = □

EMPTY SET

0 sometimes written as ∅

It is possible to form subsets of any set on this list by deleting all, some, or none of its members. If we are to begin with A, for example, delete △ and we are left with E, or ○. If we delete ○ we are left with D, or △. If we delete all members, we are left with 0. If we delete no member of set A we have A.

Using the sumbol ⊂ to denote subset, show how F⊂B, C⊂1, E⊂C. Do you know why A⊂A? We said a subset could be formed by deleting none of its members.

The empty set is a subset of every set in this small universe, and $0 \subset 1$. If X is any subset in the universe, then this may be expressed as $X \subset 1$. Every set is a subset of the universe.

Look again at the list of sets that use the symbols △, ○, and □. Do you see that D is a subset of B? We can also express this by using a diagram:

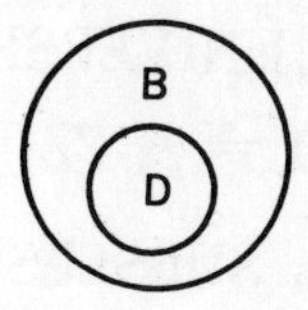

The smaller circle, D , lies wholly within the larger circle, B .

A British mathematician of the nineteenth century, John Venn, used diagrams similar to this to illustrate these relationships:

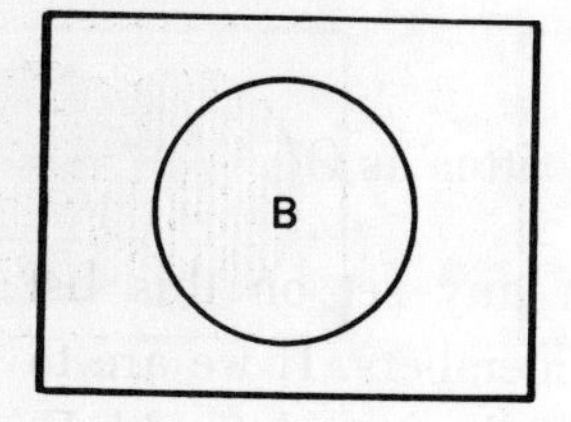

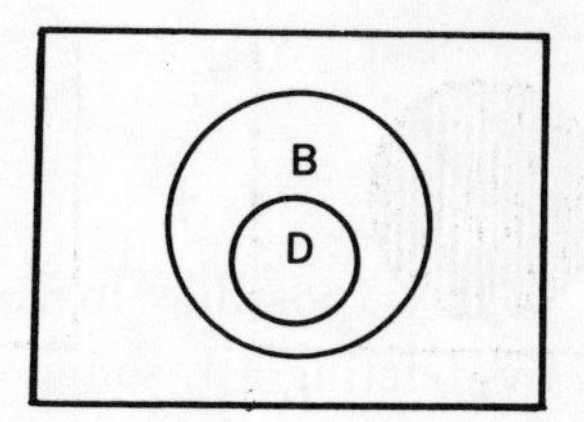

Let's perform some operations on these sets.

UNION

The first operation we will perform can best be called *union.* It is very similar to addition because it follows the

Commutative and Associative Laws of addition. But it is not addition in a numerical sense, because it is concerned with classes of objects, not numbers. For example, if you and your brother each put two dishes on the table, you have added four dishes to the table. In Boolean algebra this is only regarded as bringing about a union of members of the same set.

$$\text{Let 2 dishes} = X$$
$$X + X = 2X \text{ in algebra}$$

In Boolean algebra, X merely represents the set called dishes. $X + X$ now represents a union, in this case of members in the same set. $X + X = X$ because there are no new elements. The result is the original set; or stated simply, there are only dishes on the table.

If we wanted to create a union of two sets, $X + Y$, we would have the following:

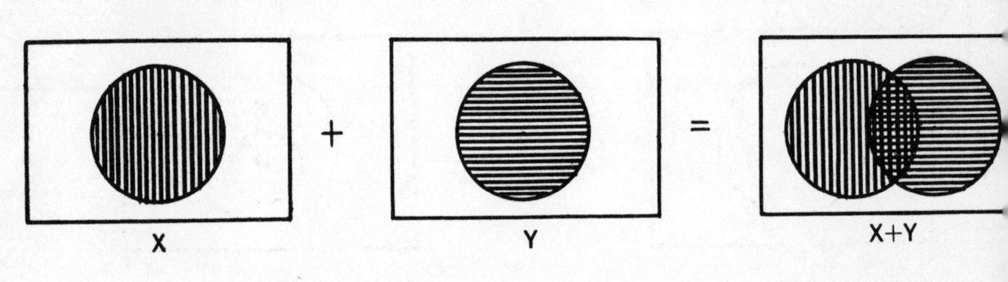

Using Venn diagrams, $X + Y$ is represented by the total area within X and Y in the third diagram.

The Commutative Law holds true because the union of X and Y yields the same result as the union of Y and X. $X + Y = Y + X$.

Can you explain how the Venn diagrams below illustrate the Associative Law?

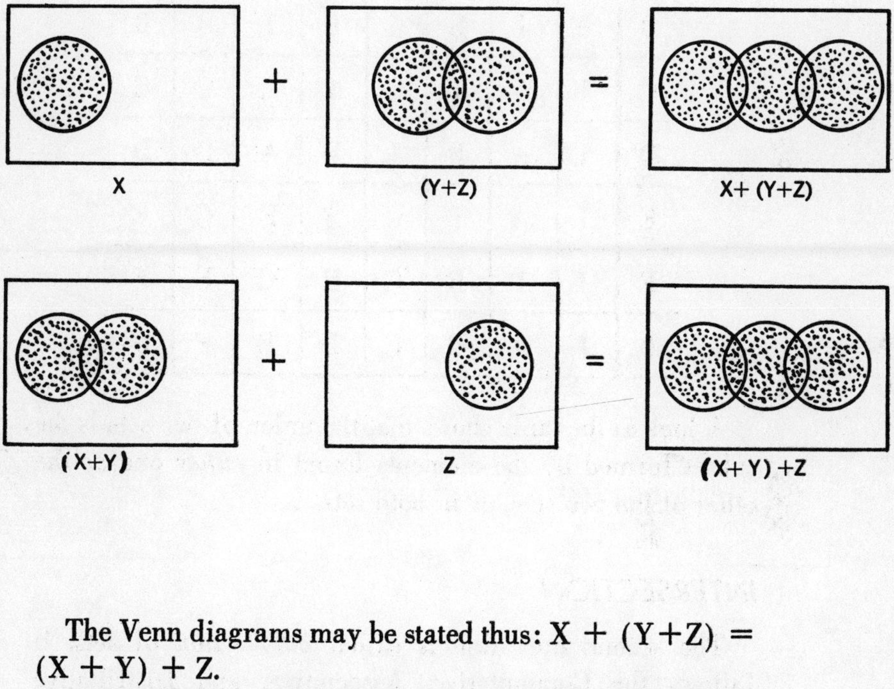

X + (Y+Z) = X+ (Y+Z)

(X+Y) + Z = (X+ Y) +Z

The Venn diagrams may be stated thus: $X + (Y+Z) = (X + Y) + Z$.

An addition, or union, table showing the results of all possible unions in the small universe given earlier might help to give us more understanding of this operation. Let the symbol $\cup$ represent union.

UNION TABLE

∪	I	A	B	C	D	E	F	0
I	I	I	I	I	I	I	I	I
A	I	A	I	I	A	A	I	A
B	I	I	B	I	B	I	B	B
C	I	I	I	C	I	C	C	C
D	I	A	B	I	D	A	B	D
E	I	A	I	C	A	E	C	E
F	I	I	B	C	B	C	F	F
0	I	A	B	C	D	E	F	0

A look at the table shows that the union of two sets is the subset formed by the elements found in *either* one *or* the other of the two sets, or in both sets.

INTERSECTION

The second operation is called *intersection* of sets. It follows the Commutative, Associative, and Distributive Laws of multiplication, which we described earlier.

If any set is multiplied by itself, the same set is the product. XX = X, not X^2, because the elements in both X and X are simply the elements in X.

The result of the multiplication of two subsets, more accurately called the intersection of two subsets, is another subset formed from the elements that are in both of the subsets being intersected. In our previous universe, for example, B contains the elements △ and □, and C contains the elements ○ and □.

A look at the multiplication (or intersection) table below shows that the intersection of B and C is F, or □, the subset formed from the elements that are common to both of the subsets, B and C.

When two subsets have no elements in common, their intersection is 0, or the empty set. Let the symbol ∩ represent intersection.

INTERSECTION TABLE

∩	I	A	B	C	D	E	F	0
I	I	A	B	C	D	E	F	0
A	A	A	D	E	D	E	0	0
B	B	D	B	F	D	0	F	0
C	C	E	F	C	0	E	F	0
D	D	D	D	0	D	0	0	0
E	E	E	0	E	0	E	0	0
F	F	0	F	F	0	0	F	0
0	0	0	0	0	0	0	0	0

In this same problem, $B \cap C = F$, let us see how the Commutative Law of multiplication applies to intersection by examining the Venn diagrams below.

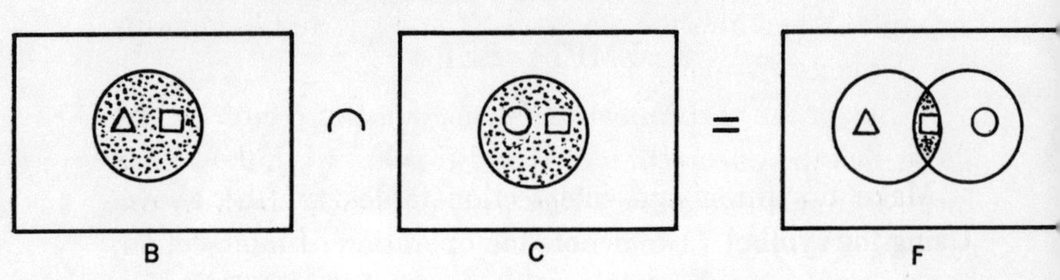

The shaded area in the last diagram illustrates the product, a set common to both B and C, and it is equally clear from the multiplication table that $B \times C = C \times B$.

The Associative Law is a bit more complicated. Let us first make up a larger universe.

UNIVERSE

1 = △ ○ □ ⬡

SUBSET

A = △ ○ □
B = △ □ ⬡
C = ○ △ ⬡
D = ○ ⬡ □
E = △ ○
F = △ □
G = △ ⬡
H = ○ □
I = ○ ⬡
J = □ ⬡
K = △

L = ○
M = □
N = ⬡

EMPTY SET
0

Make up union and intersection tables for the above. Using the symbol $\cap$ to denote the operation of intersection, can you prove that the intersection $A\cap(B\cap C) = (A\cap B)\cap C$? We will give you a clue:

$$A\cap(B\cap C) = (A\cap B)\cap C = K.$$

Here are some Venn diagrams to help you:

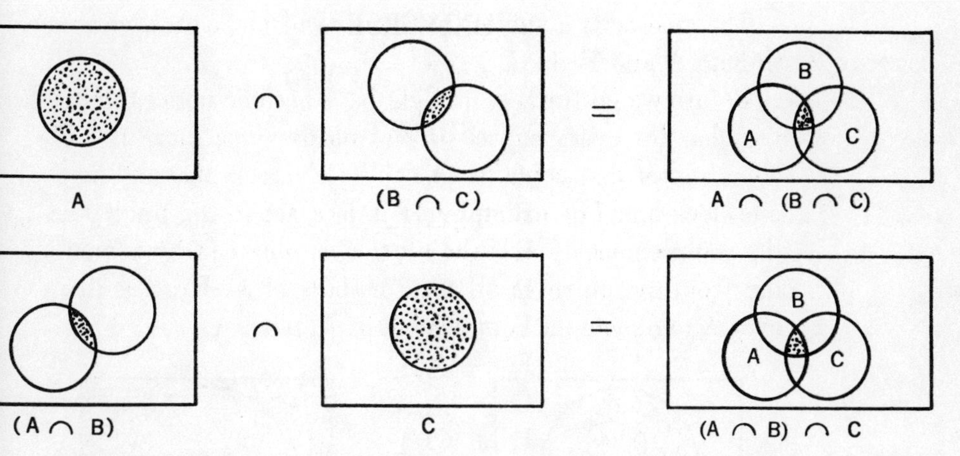

Multiplication is also distributive with respect to addition. Using the symbol to denote union, prove: $A\cap(F\cup G) = (A\cap F)\cup(A\cap G)$.

Refer to your tables.

Here are Venn diagrams to help you get a better understanding of the Distributive Law in Boolean algebra.

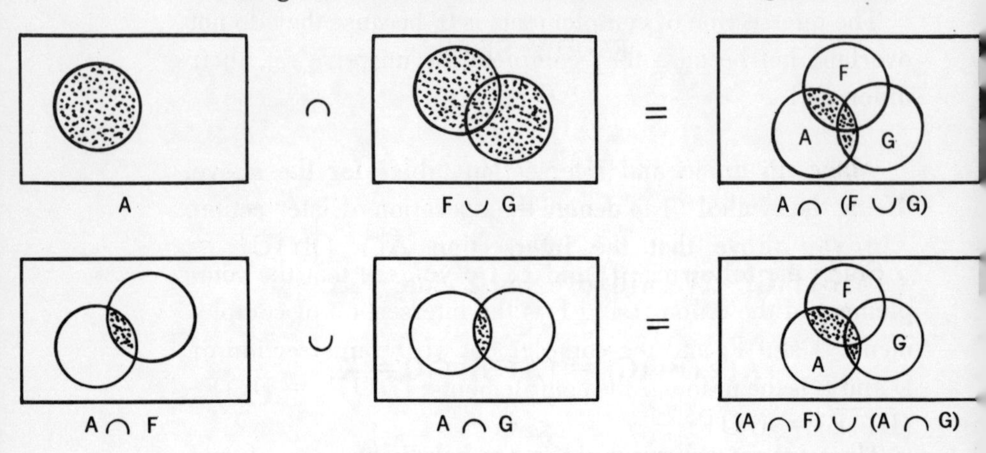

The answer is a subset that consists of elements that are in both A and F + G.

Before we go further, it might have become noticeable to you that for every subset in a given universe there is another subset that contains just those elements that the first one does not. For example: If A is a set in the universe, the complement of A is the set that is obtained by removing from the universe all the members of A. Draw a line over A to denote the complement of A, thus: $\bar{A}$.

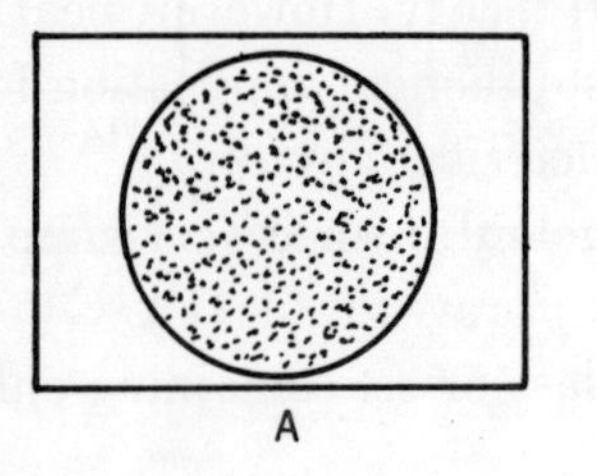

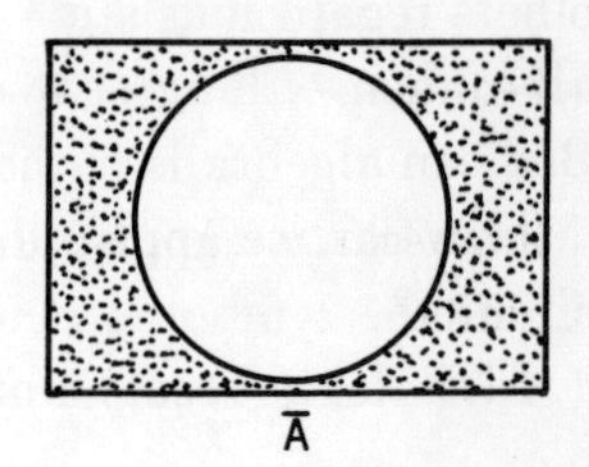

Using the last universe we constructed, 1 = △, ○, □ and ⬡, the complement of A is ______, B is ______, C is ______.

The intersection of complements is 0, because they do not overlap; but because they complete the universe set, their union is 1.

$$A \cap \bar{A} = 0$$
$$A \cup \bar{A} = 1$$

Study the following: D and F. Do you see that the complement of the union D and F is the intersection of complements $\bar{D}$ and $\bar{F}$, and the complement of the intersection of D and F is the union of the complements: $(\overline{D \cup F}) = \bar{D} \cap \bar{F}$; $(\overline{D \cap F}) = \bar{D} \cup \bar{F}$?

The truth of these rules can be seen in the fact that a union contains elements in one set *or* the other, and an intersection consists of elements in one set *and* another. The complement consists of elements *not* in the given set. Not in either D or F is the same as not in D and not in F, and not in both D and F is the same as not in D *or* not in F.

ELECTRICAL CIRCUITRY

Some of today's mathematicians see Boolean algebra as a very useful tool in the modern technological world, while others regard it as a not too useful theory. However, nearly all of them will agree that the most practical application for Boolean algebra is in the use of electrical circuitry.

How can we apply Boolean algebra to some very simple circuits?

First, let us create a universe class or set containing only one member, 1. There will be only two subsets in this universe, 1 and the empty set, 0.

Union, intersection, and complement tables for this two-valued Boolean algebra will look like this:

UNION TABLE

+	1	0
1	1	1
0	1	0

INTERSECTION TABLE

·	1	0
1	1	0
0	0	0

COMPLEMENT TABLE

X	$\overline{X}$
1	0
0	1

Do you see how the union table compares with the four basic steps in binary addition? The intersection table can also be considered as the binary multiplication table, and the complement table is the same as the complement table in the binary system.

Let us see what this means in terms of an electrical circuit.

X	$\overline{X}$
ON	OFF
OFF	ON

The above diagram illustrates the complement table. There can be only two conditions to electricity — on or off.

X and $\overline{X}$ may be regarded as two switches which operate in the following manner: Whenever X is closed, $\overline{X}$ is open, and vice versa. We can represent this complement operation in the electrical circuit as shown below:

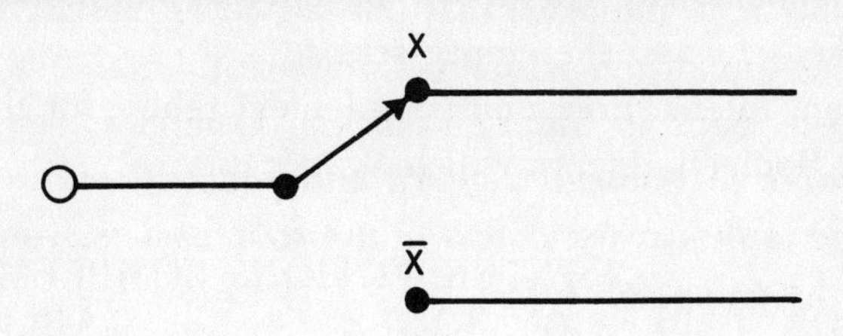

Do you remember the circuits that made decisions? Circuit B turned on the light if either one or the other or both switches were closed.

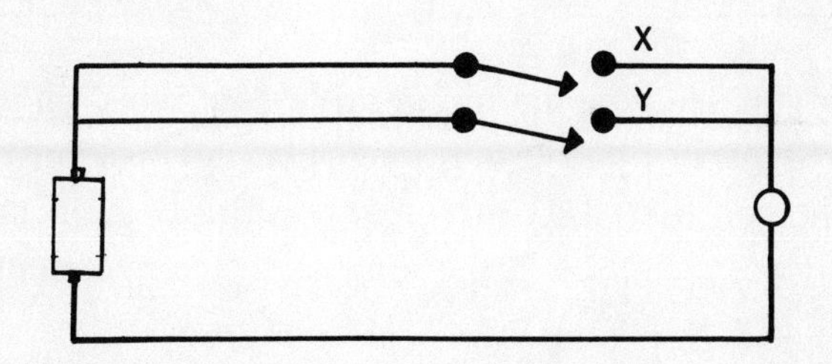

In this parallel circuit, we will call one switch X and the other Y. Do you see how this addition table applies to the circuit?

X	Y	X + Y
1	1	1
1	0	1
0	1	1
0	0	0

Of course, 1 indicates that the switch is closed; 0 indicates that the switch is open. Compare this table with the four basic steps in binary addition. Compare it with the union table in Boolean algebra and you will see that it is the same table written out to fit the four basic steps needed to add the values of X and Y.

The two switches, X and Y, can also be put in series. This is like circuit A which we discussed earlier. The light will go on only if both X and Y are closed.

Do you see how this is related to the intersection table of two-valued Boolean algebra?

Thus:

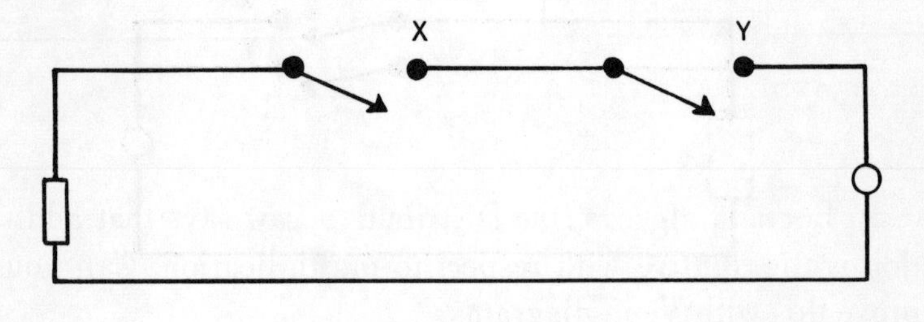

X	Y	XY
1	1	1
1	0	0
0	1	0
0	0	0

If you compare this table with the one on intersection, you will find that it is the same table written out to fit the four basic steps needed to multiply the values of X and Y.

Memorize these relationships:

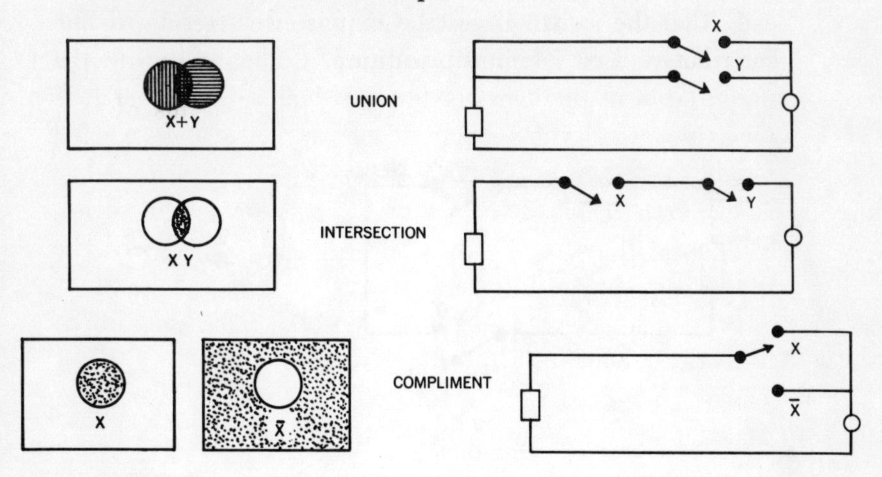

In Boolean algebra, the Distributive Law says that addition is distributive with respect to multiplication. Can you prove this with Venn diagrams?

Now for some problems:

1. Draw the circuits that prove X + Y = Y + X (the Commutative Law of addition).
2. Draw the circuits that prove (X + Y) + Z = X + (Y + Z) (the Associative Law).
3. What law do these circuits prove?

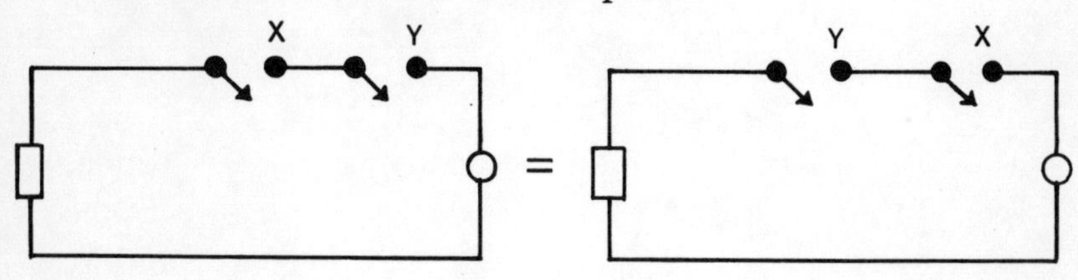

Draw the appropriate Venn diagrams.

4. Can the next circuit be expressed in terms of the Distributive Law of multiplication?

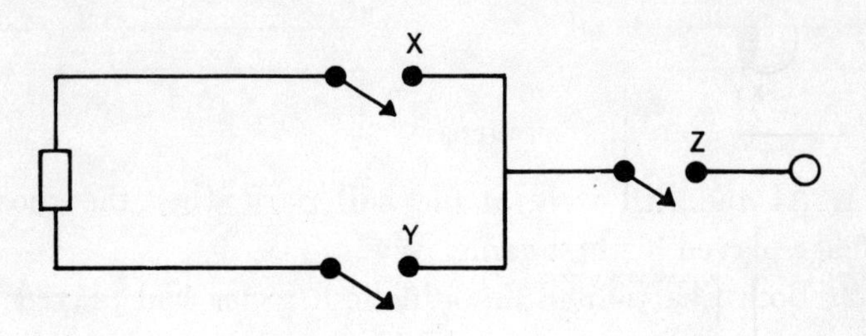

Chapter Five

MATHEMATICS IN LOGIC

Symbolic Logic

1. Al and Bill were at the ball park when the rookie pitcher played his first game.

2. Both Charlie and the athletic director had played on the same team in high school with the goalie.

3. The athletic director who scouted Dave is planning to watch Al during his next game.

4. Al doesn't know Bill.

5. One of these men is a quarterback.

Who is the athletic director; the quarterback; the pitcher; the goalie?

We will have to make some deductions from the information given in the five statements. Perhaps our best approach to this is to make a chart.

	QUARTERBACK	GOALIE	PITCHER	ATHLETIC DIRECTOR
AL	✓	X	X	X
BILL	X	X	X	✓
CHARLIE	X	X	✓	X
DAVE	X	✓	X	X

Since Al and Bill watched the pitcher, neither of them is the pitcher, so place an X in the appropriate boxes. Charlie (see 2) cannot be the goalie. Place an X in the appropriate box. Now, from statements 2 and 3 we can deduce that neither Charlie, Dave, nor Al is the athletic director; therefore, Bill is the athletic director. Mark a ✓ in the appropriate box. Since Bill is the athletic director, he is not the quarterback, goalie, or pitcher. Mark X's in the appropriate boxes. Since Al does not know Bill, he could not be the goalie either. Neither can Bill or Charlie be the goalie. Dave must be the goalie. Since Dave is the goalie, we may deduce that Al is the quarterback, and Charlie the pitcher.

To be good at mathematics, you must be able to reason logically, and there are two basic kinds of reasoning that can be used: *inductive* reasoning and *deductive* reasoning.

When our earliest astronomers traced the paths of the stars across the sky, they were not only trying to explain these paths, they were also finding patterns. Looking for a pattern in things is called inductive reasoning. Here is an example of inductive reasoning where we look for patterns and only get probable answers.

Complete the series of numbers: 2, 3, 4.
We might say the next three are: 5, 6, 7.

OR

We could conceivably say that the next three were the original numbers repeated:

2, 3, 4 — 2, 3, 4.

OR REVERSED:

2, 3, 4 — 4, 3, 2.

We can only get probable answers through induction.

Thus, finding a pattern in things is called inductive reasoning. After we find these patterns, we try to prove things about them, and that process is called deductive reasoning.

Deductive reasoning is a basic process in mathematical proof. It is often expressed in the form: *if* all the information we start with is true, *then* the conclusion is true. For example: *if* it is raining and we are standing in the rain, *then* we will get wet.

Of course, there must be an agreement on the hypothesis or information we begin with. The information provided by the hypothesis is assumed to be true. Next, we must agree on the rules used to reach conclusions. *Logic* is the study of these rules. Since we are approaching the subject of logic from the mathematicians' position, we will use symbols to guide us to our conclusions. They will act in much the same way as signs, lights, and road maps serve as instructions to motorists. Thus, the subtitle for this chapter — Symbolic Logic.

PRACTICAL APPLICATION OF SYMBOLIC LOGIC

A. Using the mathematics of logical reasoning helps our critical reading, listening, and thinking in:
   1. Newspapers, magazines, textbooks
   2. Things we hear on radio, TV, or in conversations with people
   3. All information

B. Using the mathematics of logical reasoning aids strategy and planning in:
   1. Games and puzzle solving
   2. Government (in war and peace)

3. Business (quality control)

We can learn more about symbolic logic through:

Symbols
Venn diagrams
Truth tables
Computers.

Before we study symbols, Venn diagrams, and other aids, however, let us decide what kinds of statements can be examined by symbolic logic and what kinds cannot.

A declarative sentence which states a fact and ends with a period can be used in logic. The declarative sentence must not be nonsensical. It must be meaningful. It must be either true or false, but not both.

An interrogative sentence asks a question and ends with a question mark. It is *not used* in logic. For example: "How are you?"

An imperative sentence, a sentence that gives a command and ends with a period or exclamation point, is *not used* in logic. For example: "Prepare the ship for sea."

An exclamatory sentence expresses emotion and always ends with an exclamation mark. It is *not used* in logic. For example: "How happy he looks!"

So far we are agreed that only declarative sentences are to be used in logic and that we shall be concerned with the deductive process of reasoning. At this point, Venn diagrams can serve us again. They will help us to understand the deductive process with simple declarative statements. Suppose we are expressing the concept that all monkeys are animals.

If we let M equal the set that contains all the monkeys in the world, and A the set that includes all the animals in the world, it is clear that $M \subset A$, or that M is a subset of A. Certainly not all animals in the world are monkeys, so every animal that is not a monkey would be represented by all the points outside the circle M and within the circle A.

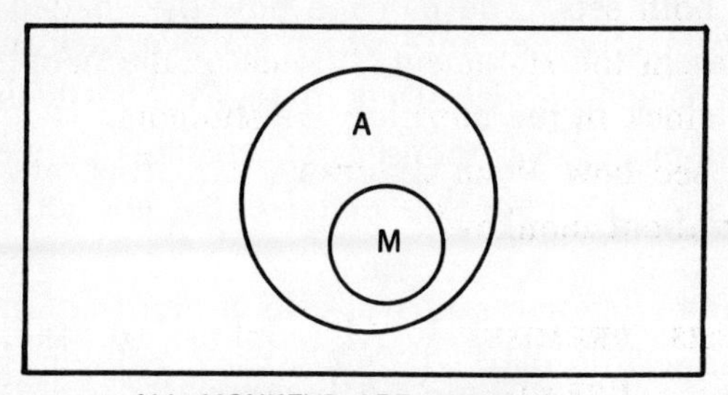

ALL MONKEYS ARE ANIMALS

We could also have several subsets of monkeys: tall monkeys, medium monkeys, and little monkeys; the Venn diagram shows this relationship. The three small circles, TM, MM, and LM, have no points in common. Obviously no monkey can be tall and little at the same time.

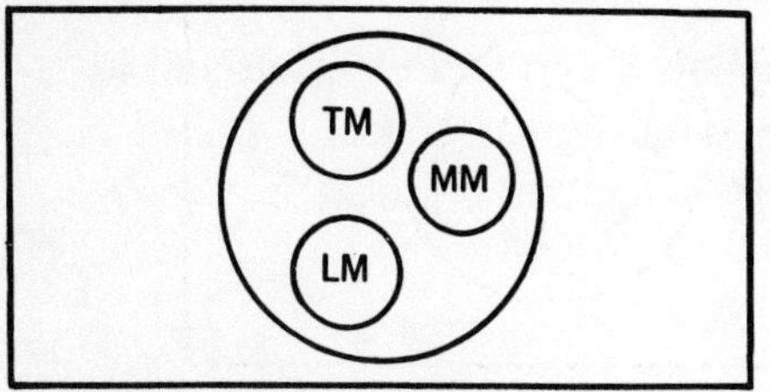

SUBSETS OF MONKEYS

We have illustrated "all" and "none" so far. But we can also use Venn diagrams to illustrate "some." For example: *Some* students get up at 8 o'clock in the morning.

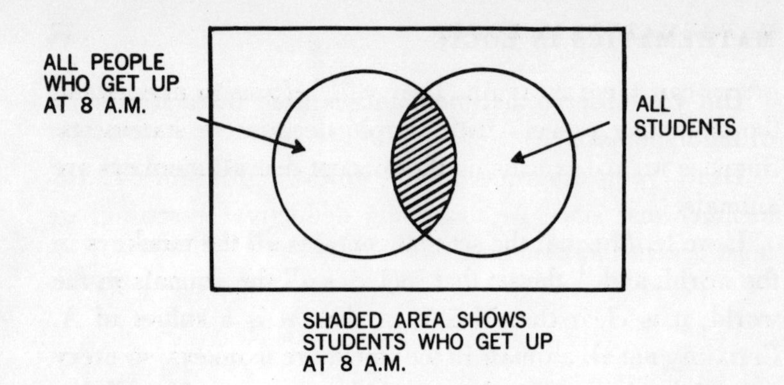

The shaded area in the overlapping circles contains elements of both sets. You can see how the shaded area can also represent the statement: "Some of the people who get up at 8 o'clock in the morning are students."

Let us see how Venn diagrams can illustrate a simple argument about monkeys:

HYPOTHESIS PREMISE: 1. All monkeys are mammals.
PREMISE: 2. All mammals are animals.

(If we accept 1 and 2 as being true, we may therefore conclude:)

CONCLUSION: All monkeys are animals.

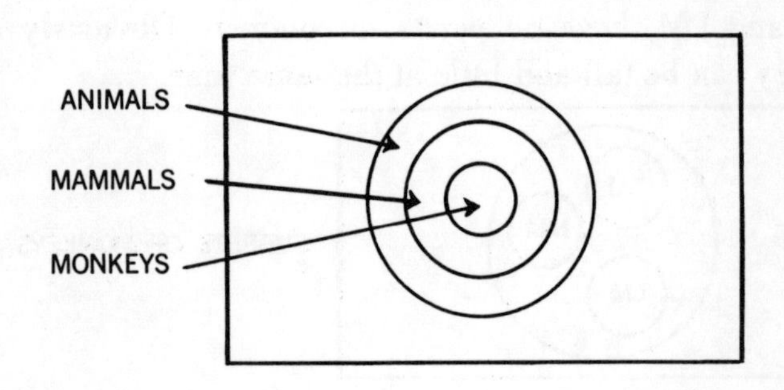

Did you observe that *mammals* is used in each premise of the hypothesis?

Draw Venn diagrams for the following arguments. Remember that since we are using deductive reasoning, we must accept the hypothesis as true.

HYPOTHESIS: 1. Man can fly through space.
2. John Glenn is a man.
CONCLUSION: John Glenn can fly through space.

Of course *man* is the word found in each hypothesis. Can you do these on your own?

HYPOTHESIS: 1. All clarinets are reed instruments.
2. All reed instruments can be played in bands.
CONCLUSION: Therefore, ______________________________
______________________________.

HYPOTHESIS: 1. All Kardies are Flazes.
2. All Flazes are Rushes.
CONCLUSION: ______________________________.

The following problem deals with "none":

HYPOTHESIS: 1. No monkeys can fly.
2. All sparrows can fly.
CONCLUSION: No monkeys are sparrows.

Expressed in Venn diagrams:

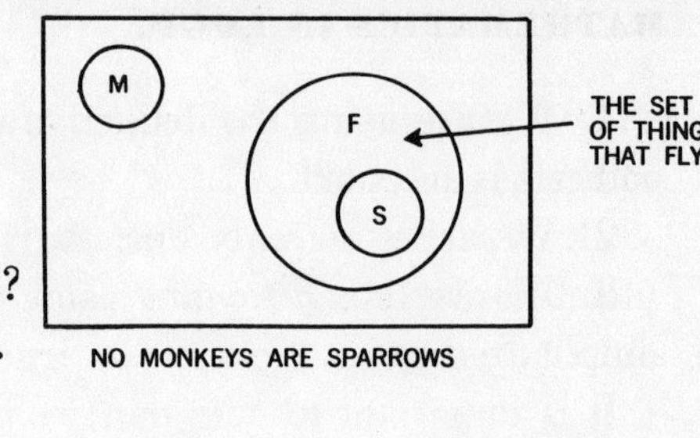

NO MONKEYS ARE SPARROWS

Can you solve this one?

No #'s are B's.
All $'s are B's.
Therefore, ______________________________.

Up to now we have been dealing with valid arguments, or those arguments which can be proven by the rules of logic, and we have illustrated these by Venn diagrams. Here is an *invalid* argument:

HYPOTHESIS: 1. Some fish bite.
2. All trout are fish.
CONCLUSION: All trout will bite.

Of course, anyone who has held a fishing line can tell you how wrong this is. Let's see how it works out with a Venn .agram.

If trout are a subset of *all* fish, we still need further information to tell us specifically that trout will bite, other-

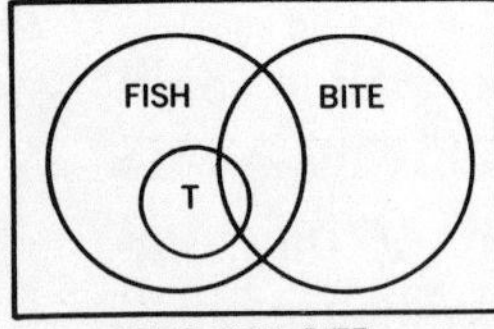

SOME FISH BITE

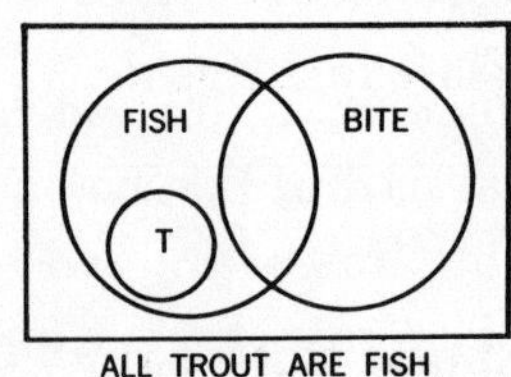

ALL TROUT ARE FISH

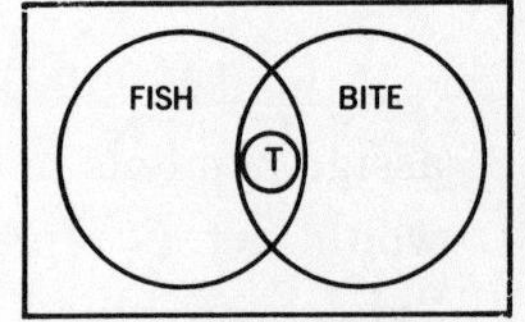

ALL TROUT WILL BITE

wise three Venn diagrams are possible. If there is more than one possible diagram no valid conclusion can be drawn.

Before we go on to more complicated arguments, we need different and more complex symbols. We have stressed several things so far:

1. We are using the deductive process in which the hypothesis is accepted.

2. We are using only declarative sentences.

3. Words like *all*, *none*, and *some* are key words in simple arguments.

It is important to note that we have been discussing the validity of an argument. Now we will examine sentences to determine their *truth* values.

First, let us state what we mean by a simple declarative sentence and a compound declarative sentence:

> A simple declarative sentence contains no connecting words such as *and*, *or*, *if*, *then*, *if and only if*, and other similar words. A simple sentence cannot be separated into other sentences as a compound sentence can. For example: *Roses are red. Violets are blue.* These are simple declarative statements.

> Compound sentences contain two or more simple sentences which are joined by connectives. For example: Roses are red *and* violets are blue. This is a compound declarative sentence.

A mathematician looking at this old familiar line could assign symbols to each part of that compound sentence. He would let *P* represent "roses are red" and *Q* represent "violets are blue." Then, "roses are red and violets are blue" could be expressed as "P and Q," where *P* and *Q* represent specific statements.

Sometimes a compound sentence contains three simple sentences: "The sun is shining and the farmer is planting, but the boys are fishing." These three statements could be represented as "P and Q and R."

Instead of writing out *and*, the mathematician uses the symbol $\wedge$, which is something like an A with the crossbar left out. The symbol $\wedge$ means *and, also, but, moreover, however, as well as, in addition to,* etc. For example: The skies are cloudy, moreover it is raining.

Let P be: The skies are cloudy.

Let Q be: It is raining.

A compound declarative sentence may be notated symbolically as $P \wedge Q$. $\wedge$ is a symbol for the *conjunction* of simple declarative sentences.

When the symbol $\wedge$ is inverted to $\vee$ it represents the connective, *or*. $\vee$ is a symbol for the *disjunction* of simple declarative sentences. However, there is something very exceptional about the connective, *or*. For example, in this sentence: "I will go to college or look for a job," it seems that one event would exclude the other. This would be called the *exclusive* use of *or*.

Or has another *inclusive* meaning as well. In the sentence, "Five is less than 8 *or* 8 is greater than 5," these conditions are not mutually exclusive. *Or* means both:

Let P be: $5 < 8$
Let Q be: $8 > 5$
Then: $P \vee Q$.

We shall always use $\vee$, the inclusive meaning of *or*, to mean *either or both*. When we wish to make certain that *or* does not mean both, we shall state *either/or*, but not *both*.

Not is a connective that negates or denies the truth or even the falseness of a declarative sentence. The symbol for not is $\sim$. It also means: *it is not true, it is not the case,* etc.

Do you understand the symbolic notation below the next sentence?

"It is not the case that (roses are blue and violets are red)."

$$\sim (P \wedge Q)$$

Parentheses are used to bring out the entire subject to be negated.

A familiar type of compound sentence may be formed by using the connectives, *if* and *then.* First, look at two simple sentences:

A stone is thrown into the pond.
It will sink.

Now rewrite these two sentences as one compound sentence, using *if* and *then:*

If a stone is thrown into the pond, *then* it will sink.

This type of declarative compound sentence is called a *conditional* sentence, and is expressed as follows:

Let P be: A stone is thrown into the pond.
Let Q be: It will sink.

Then $P \rightarrow Q$ is the symbolic expression for the conditional sentence. Substitute the following meanings for the arrow: *implies, is sufficient for, is necessary for.*

Take this conditional sentence, represent the statements symbolically, and substitute the other meanings given above for the arrow:

"If the ball player is Stan Musial, then he hit over .300 in 1958." It becomes very evident that $P \rightarrow Q$. On the other hand, it would be a serious error in logic to assume $Q \rightarrow P$, or that if he hit over .300 in 1958 the ball player was Stan Musial. Other ball players hit over .300 in 1958. In other words, the rule of logic we are concerned with here is that when the antecedent (P) is exchanged with the consequent (Q), the *form* of the sentence has not changed, *the meaning has*. The resulting sentence is called the *converse* of the original conditional sentence.

Let P be: The subject is a bird.
Let Q be: The subject has two legs.

To make a conditional sentence out of the above and then write out its converse —

$$P \rightarrow Q, Q \rightarrow P.$$

There are occasions when the converse of $P \rightarrow Q$, $Q \rightarrow P$ is also true. These sentences are called *biconditional* sentences. $(P \rightarrow Q) \wedge (Q \rightarrow P)$ can be changed to $P \longleftrightarrow Q$. $\longleftrightarrow$ is read, "if and only if." A triangle is equilateral *if and only if* the triangle has three equal sides.

Let P be: A triangle is equilateral.
Let Q be: The triangle has three equal sides.

P implies Q, and Q implies P, or $(P \rightarrow Q) \wedge (Q \rightarrow P)$. The symbolic expression is $P \longleftrightarrow Q$.

Now substitute the following meanings for $\longleftrightarrow$: *a necessary and sufficient condition for, equivalent to.* Do you see that $P \rightarrow Q$ and its converse $Q \rightarrow P$ are both true?

Instead of using P, Q, and R to represent specific statements, let us use the lower case letters as place holders for statements. Because modern logic can be expressed in symbolic notation, $p \wedge q$ becomes an open sentence or statement formula in which the letters and the symbol $\wedge$ can be exchanged for the appropriate statements or propositions.

Let us review our symbols using p and q:

$p \wedge q$ is the conjunction of p and q.
$p \vee q$ is the disjunction of p and q.
$\sim p$ is the negation of p.
$p \longrightarrow q$ is the conditional that p implies q where p is the antecedent and q the consequent.
$p \longleftrightarrow q$ is a biconditional or equivalence relationship. It means that p and q are both true or both false.

We have agreed that sentences in logic should be either true or false, but not both. Let us consider all the possibilities of T and F (true and false) in the $p \wedge q$ relationship:

p is true and q is true.
p is true and q is false.
p is false and q is true.
p is false and q is false.

This distribution of information can be organized into a table for conjunctions. This table is called a *truth table.* While Venn diagrams help us to picture simple arguments, a truth table provides us with a better tool for investigating more complicated arguments.

TRUTH TABLE FOR CONJUNCTIONS

p	q	$p \wedge q$
T	T	T
T	F	F
F	T	F
F	F	F

Can you see a relationship between this table and the ON-OFF condition of an electrical circuit?

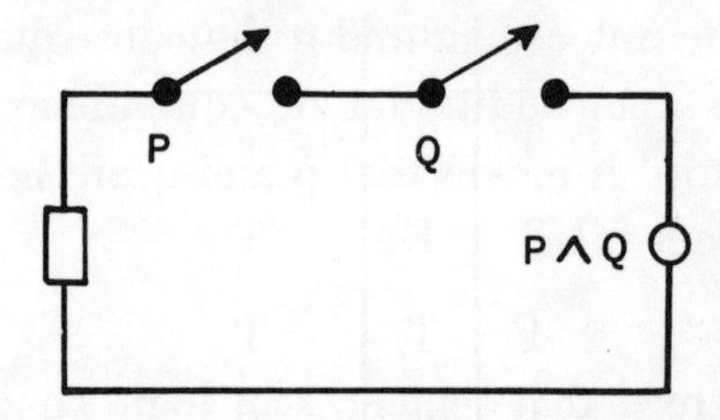

If T can be translated into the ON condition of an electric current, $p \wedge q$ can be T only if p is T and q is T. If p is T and q is T, then the current will flow through the circuit. In the conjunction truth table, when both p and q are true, then $p \wedge q$ is true.

The truth values for negations are easy to identify. There are two possible combinations for negation:

TRUTH TABLE FOR NEGATION

	p	~p
When p is T then ~p is F.	T	F
When p is F then ~p is T.	F	T

The electrical design for negation involves an *inverter*, or a device that will invert the current. In other words, in a circuit dealing with negations, the condition of the current must be changed. When the current is ON the inverter puts it OFF. When the current is OFF the inverter allows it to flow.

In disjunctive sentences, using the connective *or*, $p \vee q$ is true if at least one of the sentences or statements is true. This table for disjunction gives all possible cases of p and q.

TRUTH TABLE FOR DISJUNCTION

p	q	$p \vee q$
T	T	T
T	F	T
F	T	T
F	F	F

Suppose we had four statements with two being true and two being false:

Let P be: Snow is white.
Let Q be: Brazil is within the Arctic Circle.
Let R be: All cats fly.
Let S be: $5 > 3$.

Find the truth values for the following:

$$P \vee Q, \quad Q \vee R, \quad Q \wedge R, \quad P \wedge S,$$

$$(P \wedge S) \vee Q, \qquad (Q \wedge R) \vee (R \vee S)$$

Can you describe the circuit below in terms of a disjunctive sentence?

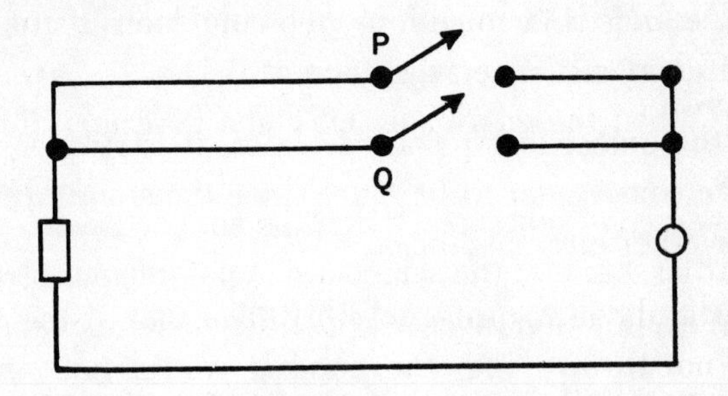

In a conditional sentence, or sentence of implication, the truth value is determined by relationships expressed in the conditional truth table as follows:

CONDITIONAL TRUTH TABLE

p	q	p → q
T	T	T
T	F	F
F	T	T
F	F	T

When the antecedent is true and the consequent is false,

the conditional sentence is false. In the other three cases it is true.

Consider the four possibilities of: "If a stone is thrown into the pond, it will sink."

If both antecedent and consequent phrases are true, then certainly the conditional sentence is *true.*

If only the consequent phrase is false, then the sentence is *false.* Obviously, if the stone doesn't sink, this conditional sentence is untrue.

If the antecedent phrase is false, it is still possible for the consequent to be *true,* since the stone can sink under other circumstances.

Certainly it is quite possibly *true* that if the stone were not thrown into the pond it would not sink. It would be possible to assume another disposition of the stone, i.e., it could be placed on the ground, carried home, etc.

Here is the truth table for a biconditional sentence. Refer back to the equilateral triangle and think out each of the four possibilities.

BICONDITIONAL TRUTH TABLE

p	q	$p \longleftrightarrow q$
T	T	T
T	F	F
F	T	F
F	F	T

Now let us see how the biconditional table may be derived from the conditional table:

p	q	$p \rightarrow q$	$q \rightarrow p$ (converse)	$(p \rightarrow q) \wedge (q \rightarrow p)$ or $p \longleftrightarrow q$
T	T	T	T	T
T	F	F	T	F
F	T	T	F	F
F	F	T	T	T

The last column was obtained by using the values of $p \rightarrow q$ and $q \rightarrow p$ and applying the Truth Table for Conjunctions.

TAUTOLOGIES

There are some propositional forms or compound declarative sentences that are true no matter what values are assigned to the individual statements or simple sentences. Such a compound sentence is called a *tautology* and contains all T's in the final column of its truth table. A tautology is a basic tool used by mathematicians for determining the validity of arguments.

If one F occurs in the last column of the truth table, the compound sentence is not a tautology. If all the values in the last column are F's, the compound sentence is called a *contradiction*.

Before we construct truth tables for tautologies, let us describe the parts that make up a truth table. A truth table contains columns which read vertically and rows which read horizontally. For example: When we have a simple sentence, p is the designation for the column and T and F each occupy a row.

p
T
F

Here is the truth table for a compound sentence made up of two simple sentences, p and q. This table contains all the possibilities for T and F when p and q are under consideration.

p	q
T	T
T	F
F	T
F	F

If we were considering all the possibilities of three different simple sentences or statements, p, q, and r, the following table would be needed.

p	q	r
T	T	T
T	T	F
T	F	T
T	F	F
F	T	T
F	T	F
F	F	T
F	F	F

Have you noticed any patterns? Each time we add another statement the rows in the truth table increase to the next power of 2 (2, 4, 8). If we were considering four simple sentences we would use 16 rows.

Now let us construct a truth table to determine whether a statement formula is a tautology or not. Remember that p, in this case, will be regarded as a place holder.

Is $\sim(\sim p) \longleftrightarrow p$ a tautology? The truth table to prove this is formed as follows:

p	$\sim p$	$\sim(\sim p)$	$\sim(\sim p) \longleftrightarrow p$
T	F	T	T
F	T	F	T

1. Under p enter the values for p.
2. Under $\sim p$ list the values for $\sim p$ as found in the truth table for negation.
3. Using the definition of $\sim$, or negation, we can now fill in the column for $\sim(\sim p)$.
4. Use column p and the column designated $\sim(\sim p)$ and the biconditional truth table to form the last column, $\sim(\sim p) \longleftrightarrow p$.

Since there are no F's in the last column, $\sim(\sim p) \longleftrightarrow p$ *is* a tautology. Actually, this tautology has a name. It is called the *law of the double negative.* Do you remember that a double negative in English is equivalent to a positive statement? Further, if you have had algebra, you know that the product of two negative numbers is a positive number.

Let's try another: Is $p \longleftrightarrow (p \vee q)$ a tautology?

p	q	$(p \vee q)$	$p \longleftrightarrow (p \vee q)$
T	T	T	T
T	F	T	T
F	T	T	F
F	F	F	T

The column designated $(p \vee q)$ is computed as the q in the biconditional table. Because there is at least one F in the last column, $p \longleftrightarrow (p \vee q)$ is *not* a tautology.

Write out the truth table for $(p \wedge q) \longleftrightarrow \sim (p \wedge q)$. If you do the work carefully, you will find that $(p \wedge q) \longleftrightarrow \sim (p \wedge q)$ is a contradiction.

Here are some well-known tautologies. Can you verify them?

$p \rightarrow p \vee q$	Law of addition
$p \wedge q \rightarrow p$	Law of simplification
$\sim (p \wedge \sim p)$	Law of contradiction
$[(p \rightarrow q) \wedge (q \rightarrow r)] \rightarrow (p \rightarrow r)$	Law of hypothetical syllogism

Here is an application of a tautology: A farmer is concerned about the rotation of his crops. He decides to plant corn. Is his conclusion valid?

> If alfalfa shouldn't, then beets would. It is not possible that alfalfa should and corn couldn't at the same time. If beets would then alfalfa should and corn could. Therefore corn could.

If an agricultural expert were involved with this knotty problem, he might begin thus: Let P be: alfalfa should
Let Q be: beets would
Let R be: corn could

(~ P ⟶ Q) ∧
If alfalfa shouldn't then beets would. It is not

~(P ∧ ~ R) ∧
possible that alfalfa should and corn couldn't at the same time.
[Q ⟶ (P ∧ R)] ⟶
If beets would then alfalfa should and corn could. Therefore
R
corn could.

Using symbolic logic: $(\sim p \rightarrow q) \wedge \sim (p \wedge \sim r) \wedge [q \rightarrow (p \wedge r)] \rightarrow r$. Is this a tautology? Be sure to make a truth table. Remember that two sentences can be joined by and " ∧ " instead of being separated by a period.

Every argument has a corresponding conditional sentence. In the conditional sentence, the antecedent represents the premise or premises, the consequent represents the conclusion of the argument. Arguments have more structure, more symbolic notation than conditional sentences that are not arguments. Let us see what this means by the way in which we deal with the following statements:

Let P be: It was warm yesterday.
Let Q be: The swimming pool was open.
Let R be: The boys were happy.

If we arrange these statements as follows:

1. If it was warm yesterday then the swimming pool was open. $(P \rightarrow Q)$
2. If the swimming pool was open the boys were happy. $(Q \rightarrow R)$

we have conditional sentences that do not represent arguments.

Now, let us arrange these statements to illustrate conditional sentences that do represent arguments. These new arrangements are necessary because they contain two or more related premises and their conclusion. Further, we can test the validity of these conclusions by proving that the argument does or does not yield a tautology.

1. If (it was warm yesterday or the swimming pool was open) and (it was not warm yesterday) then the swimming pool was not open.

   Express in symbolic notation:

   ___

2. If (it was warm yesterday) and (if it was warm yesterday, then the swimming pool was open) and (if the swimming pool was open, then the boys were happy) then the boys were happy.

   Symbolic notation:

   ___

3. If it was warm yesterday then (it was warm yesterday or the swimming pool was open).

   Symbolic notation:

   ___

Arguments are often given by listing the premises of the hypothesis. The sentence containing the conclusion is sometimes preceded by the symbol, $\therefore$, which means *therefore.* For example:

1. Roses are red or violets are blue.
2. Roses are not red.

The conclusion $\therefore$ Violets are blue.

The two related premises are: If P is: Roses are red.
Q is: Violets are blue.

We can write out the argument in symbolic notation:

HYPOTHESIS: 1. $P \vee Q$
2. $\sim P$
CONCLUSION: $\therefore \quad Q$

Let us make a conditional sentence corresponding to this argument:

If (roses are red or violets are blue) and
(roses are not red) then violets are blue.

In symbolic notation this means: $[(P \vee Q) \wedge \sim P] \rightarrow Q$. Is this a tautology, and is the conclusion valid?

Can you do this on your own? Be sure to separate the sentences into two premises and state your conclusion.

It is raining. If it is raining then the sky is cloudy.

Is the following argument valid?

$$\begin{array}{r} p \wedge \sim q \\ \sim p \\ \hline \therefore \sim p \end{array}$$

Illustrate the following by Venn diagrams:

Profiteers are not patriots.
Mr. Y is a profiteer.
Mr. Y is not patriotic.

Let us examine a problem with three statements in relation to an electrical circuit.

Let P be: Roses are red.
Let Q be: Violets are blue.
Let R be: Sugar is bitter.

P and Q are true (T) and R is false (F). If we write $(P \wedge Q) \wedge R$, the switch at *R* must remain open because R is false. Further, the current will not be able to turn on the light at *X*. Symbolic logic $(P \wedge Q) \wedge R$ means:

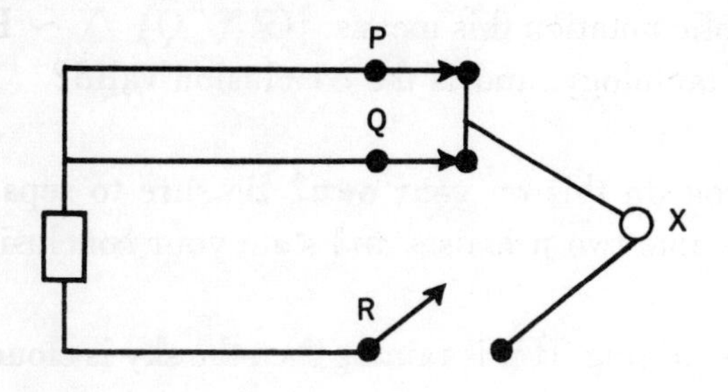

$(P \wedge Q)$ is T and R is F. On the truth table for conjunctions, a T and an F produce an F. Can you tell the truth value of $Q \wedge R$; of $P \wedge R$?

Prove the following by first making a conditional correspondence to the argument. Express this new sentence in symbolic form, then test its validity by making a truth table.

> Democrats have a majority or Republicans debate.
> Democrats have a minority.
> Republicans debate.

Chapter Six

"RUBBER SHEET GEOMETRY"

Topology

TOPOLOGY is a branch of mathematics that seems to be so full of tricks, puzzles, and impossibilities that it is almost pure magic. This branch of mathematics is really an unfinished story because mathematicians are still puzzled about some of its aspects. As a matter of fact, you may read this chapter as you would read a story; but don't read fast, and keep pencil, paper, rubber bands, scissors, string, a few doughnuts, and an old inner tube within reach. They will help you to understand better what you are reading.

The American Indians used some principles of topology when they prepared for cold weather. They would kill a bear or a deer. Then, to make their winter clothing, they would take the hide, which had once belonged to a four-legged animal, and put it around a two-legged one, very often with the skin side outside, and the furry side inside.

The animal skin was an object that had lines, points, and angles. When we studied Euclidean geometry, we learned that lengths, shapes, and angles do not change. Topology is like a geometry whose points, lines, and angles are permitted a great deal of motion, especially when the Indian was chasing other bears. The figures in topology can shrink, stretch, bend, or be distorted in almost any way. Perhaps that is why topology has earned the nickname of Rubber Sheet Geometry.

Let's use a "rubber sheet" to see what this means. An old inner tube should do. Cut out a piece of rubber from the tube about 6 by 6 inches. Draw a circle on this sheet with a piece of chalk. Place a dot in its center, and four dots outside the circle. Now, pull or stretch this sheet of rubber any way you like:

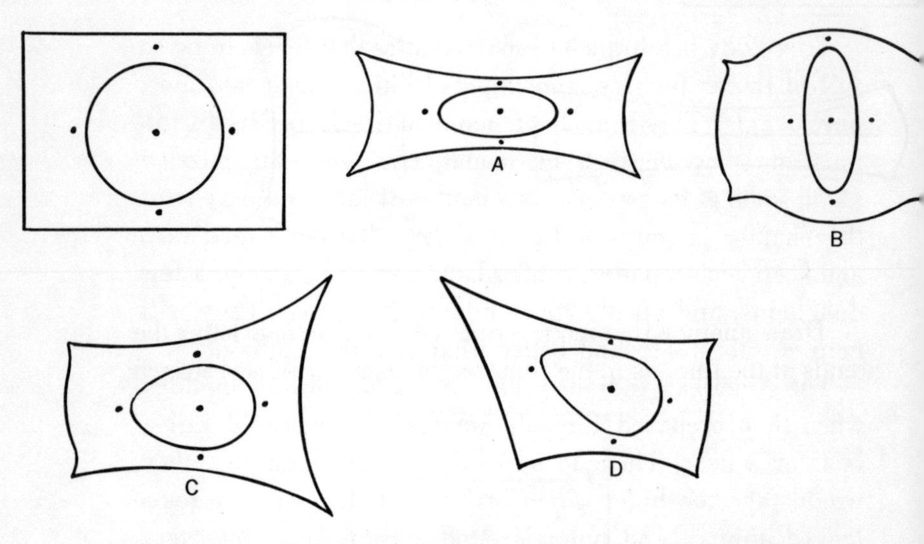

Although the circle changes its shape and size, two things do not change. The inner dot cannot be moved outside the circle, nor can any one of the four outside dots be pushed, pulled, or stretched to cross the line into the circle. In fact, we can state that in this particular topological figure, all points that lie inside the figure remain inside, and all points that lie outside must remain outside.

Now erase the circle and draw a straight line on the rubber sheet. Again, if we stretch or pull this line, its length changes and quite possibly its characteristic of being straight changes. We can make the line longer or shorter, or even make it curve:

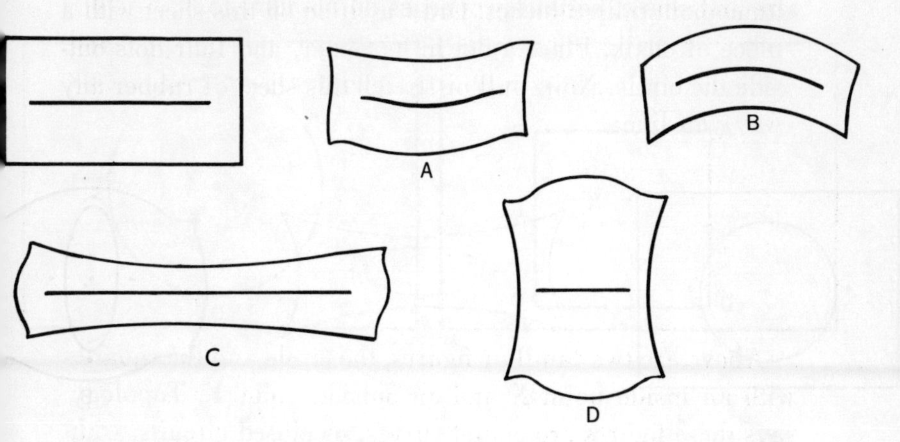

Draw another line intersecting the first line and letter the ends of the lines as in the illustration. Again pull and stretch

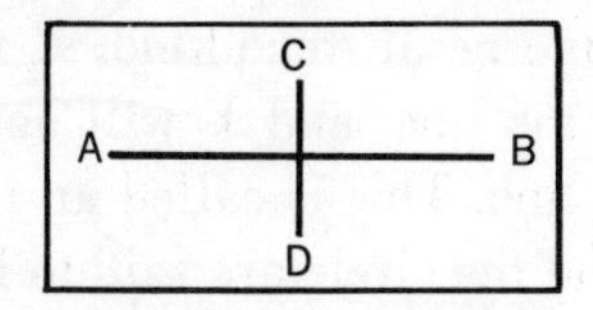

the rubber sheet. One thing will remain true. No matter how we distort the original figure, *AB* remains a path that does not cross itself. The intersection of the two lines still exists no matter how you stretch or pull the rubber sheet. In topology, line AB and line CD are called *arcs* AB and CD.

In Euclidean geometry, two figures are said to be *congruent* if all parts match when placed one on top of the other. Topology gives figures that are *equivalent,* that is to say they have similar properties.

In Euclidean geometry, we study forms that do not change in size or shape. In topology, although objects can change in size and shape, certain properties do not change.

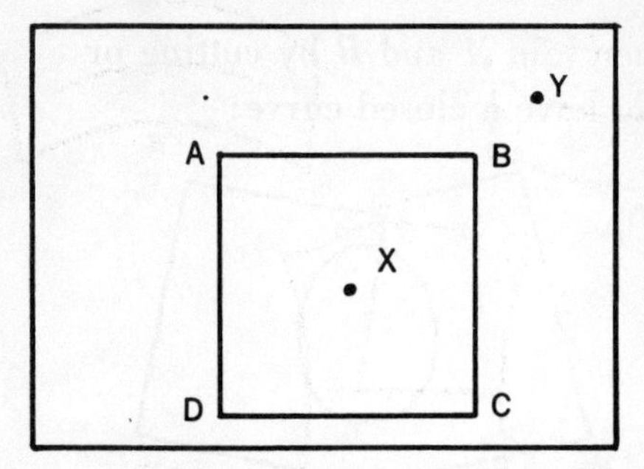

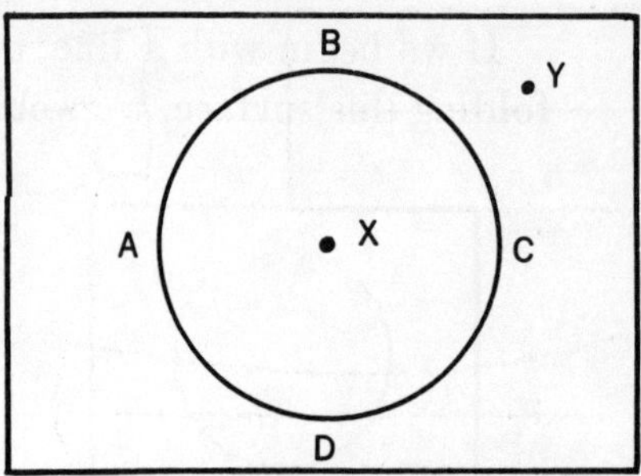

Above are two familiar figures, the circle and the square, with an inside point X and an outside point *Y*. Topology says these figures are closed curves, or closed circuits, with two arcs, *ABC* and *ADC*. No matter how we distort or make *topological transformations,* the relationship of *ABCDA* with X and *Y* will not change. While *ABCDA* will always form a continuous line of some kind, *X* will not be able to break outside of the line, and *Y* will not be able to sneak inside the closed line. This is called an *invariant* situation, and the square and the circle are said to be equivalent.

Of course, we could knock out one side of the square, or cut an arc out of the circle. If we cut, tear, or punch holes in a line, surface, or closed circuit, the topological figure has not been *transformed,* rather we have made a new topological figure. For example: If we begin with a triangle, then fold the sheet, we are left with a line:

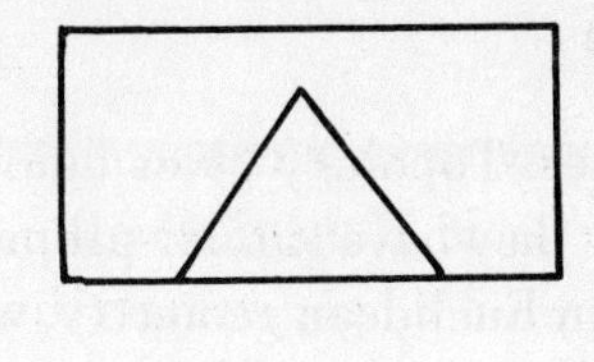

If we begin with a line, then join *A* and *B* by cutting or folding this surface, we would have a closed curve:

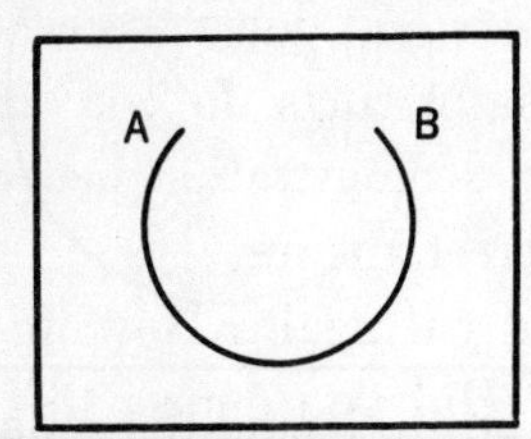

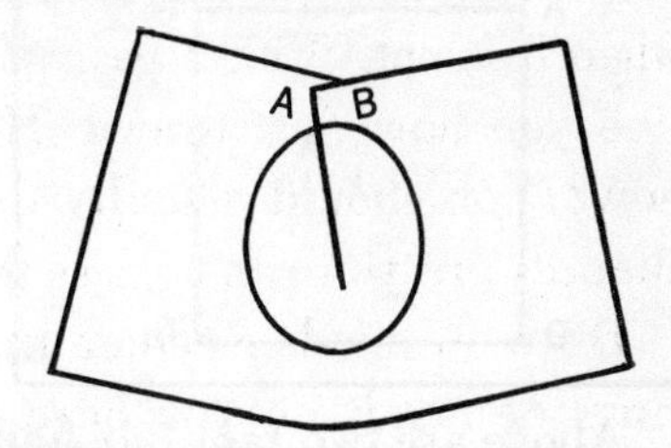

THE MOEBIUS STRIP

So far, we have been working with flat, two-dimensional problems on one side of a rubber sheet. There is another interesting aspect of topology that also involves a flat surface where the figure has only one side and an edge. Take a strip of paper about one inch wide and one foot long. Can you make a continuous line *on both sides* without lifting the pencil or crossing an edge?

Make a band from this strip, but before you do, give the end marked *B* a half twist. Now glue or tape the ends together: Does this figure have a top or bottom, front or back?

Now draw a continuous line along the center of the strip. The ends of the line will meet each other and you will have drawn a single straight line on *one* surface! An ant could walk from one point to another without having to cross over an edge.

This strip of paper is called the *Moebius strip*, named after a German mathematician of the nineteenth century. Some surprising things can happen to this Moebius strip when it is cut. With a pair of scissors, cut down the center line you have just drawn. How many rings do you have now? You should actually do this demonstration because chances are you can't guess the correct answer.

Draw in another center line and cut again. How many rings or bands do you have now? Did you expect this to happen?

Make another Moebius strip. This time begin cutting at a point one third of the way from an outside edge. Keep cutting at this one-third distance from the edge. What did you come up with this time?

Make another Moebius strip, but instead of a one-half twist, make a full twist. Cut at the middle, or cut at the one-third point. How many strips do you have now?

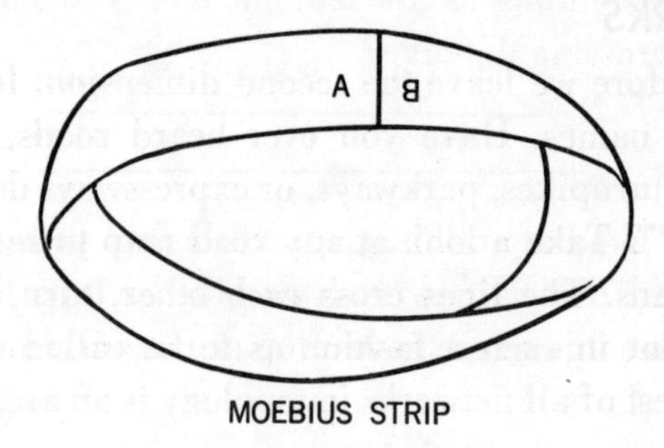

MOEBIUS STRIP

If you wish, you can make up your own variations of this as magicians have been doing for years; but for now let us look at some interesting applications. Here is a problem that has no solution in a two-dimensional flat surface.

An electronics engineer must connect corresponding numbers without crossing any of the lines.

This problem can be solved on the two dimensions of a Moebius strip. Try it. Be sure to draw the lines all the way along the strip.

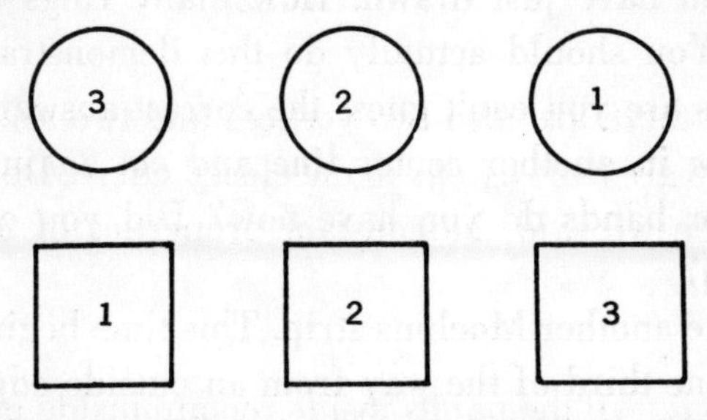

Before we leave the Moebius strip, take your watch and slide it along the strip. If your watch says 12:15 at point A, what times does it read at point B? Remember that when it reaches point B, it will be upside down and backwards!

NETWORKS

And, before we leave the second dimension, let us learn some new names. Have you ever heard roads, thruways, highways, turnpikes, parkways, or expressways described as "networks"? Take a look at any road map to see what this really means. The lines cross each other, turn, twist, and weave about in such a fashion as to be called a network. The simplest of all networks in topology is an arc, described by a straight line A___B. Points *A* and *B* are called *vertices* of this arc.

Another simple network is a closed curve: A B

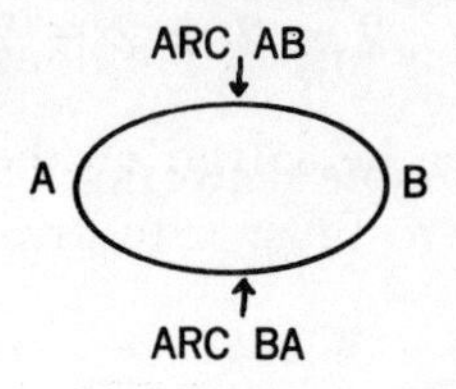

Here there are also two vertices and two arcs:

There are two *regions* to the closed curve. Do you remember when we said the constant properties of a topological figure are:

1. All the points inside remain inside in any topological transformation.
2. All the points outside remain outside in any topological transformation.

In the closed circle, there are two regions, one inside and one outside. There is only one region for a straight line, open curve, or single arc. Since there can be no inside, that region contains all the points outside the single arc.

A very famous mathematician, Leonhard Euler, expressed the relationship of vertices, arcs, and regions in the following formula:

$$V - A + R = 2.$$

Let us see if this holds true for a single arc A___B. There are two vertices, from which we subtract one arc and then add one region. Of course, the answer is: $2 - 1 + 1 = 2$. Can you apply this formula to the closed curve?

$$2 - 2 + 2 = 2$$

A B

Here are some simple networks:

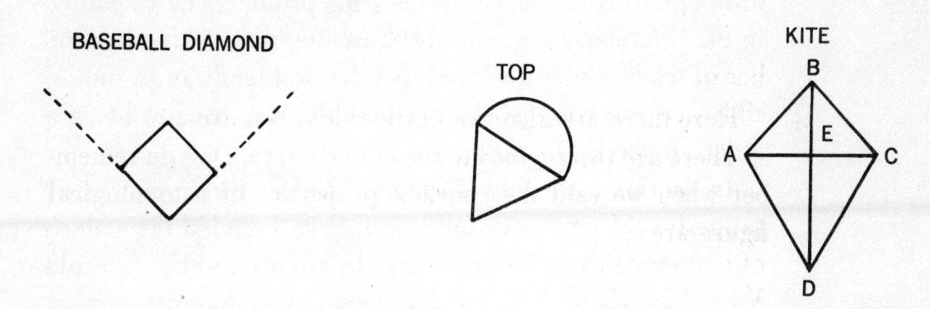

Can you apply Euler's formula to these networks?

The study of networks was probably the beginning of the study of topology. In the eighteenth century, in the university town of Königsberg (later renamed Kaliningrad by Russia), a very interesting puzzle was posed.

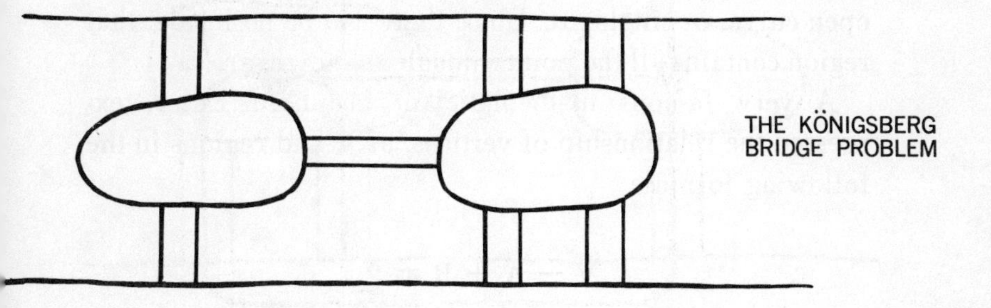

THE KÖNIGSBERG BRIDGE PROBLEM

The Preger River was cut by two islands and seven bridges, as shown in the illustration. Someone apparently tried to take his Sunday afternoon stroll by trying to cross the seven bridges by crossing each bridge only once. Not only did this keep him busy on Sunday afternoons, but it caused other people in Königsberg to walk and ponder and walk even more.

Soon the problem came to the attention of Euler. He didn't go to Königsberg to study the problem; he remained in St. Petersburg and simply drew diagrams. After a number of trials, Euler declared that the problem was an impossible one and Königsberg presumably went back to being a quiet university town.

In working out his diagrams, Euler discovered many properties of networks and in doing so founded the branch of mathematics called topology. In addition to the formula $V - A + R = 2$, Euler discovered other important properties of networks. We shall use the Königsberg Bridge problem to illustrate these properties.

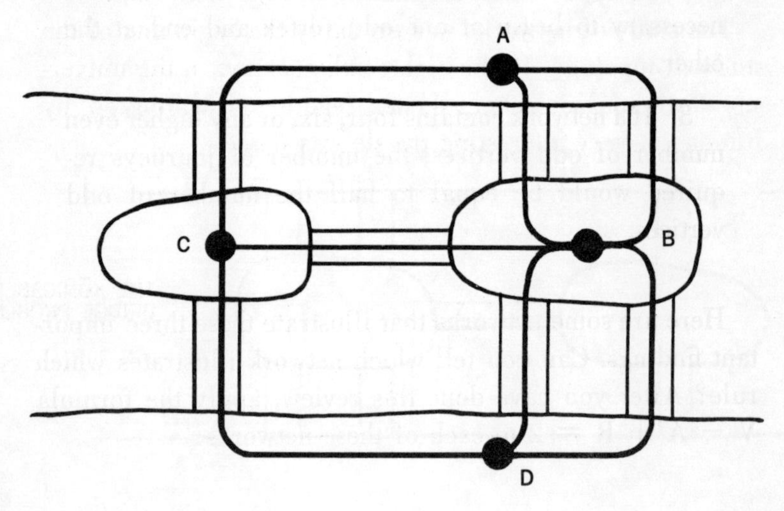

The vertices in the bridge problem are A, B, C, D. The number of arcs belonging to vertex C are three. Euler called this an *odd* vertex. In fact, for each vertex in the Königsberg Bridge network there is an odd number of arcs. Euler discovered that this matter of the odd or even number of arcs to a vertex is the key to solving a network problem that must only be traveled once.

Remember: An *odd* vertex has an *odd* number of arcs.
An *even* vertex has an *even* number of arcs.

Consider these findings by Euler:

1. A network consisting of even vertices can be traveled in one journey, returning to the starting point.

2. If a network contains two, and only two, odd vertices, it can be traveled in one journey. However, it is necessary to begin at one odd vertex and end at the other.

3. If a network contains four, six, or any higher even number of odd vertices, the number of journeys required would be equal to half the number of odd vertices.

Here are some networks that illustrate these three important findings. Can you tell which network illustrates which rule? After you have done this review, apply the formula $V - A + R = 2$ to each of these networks:

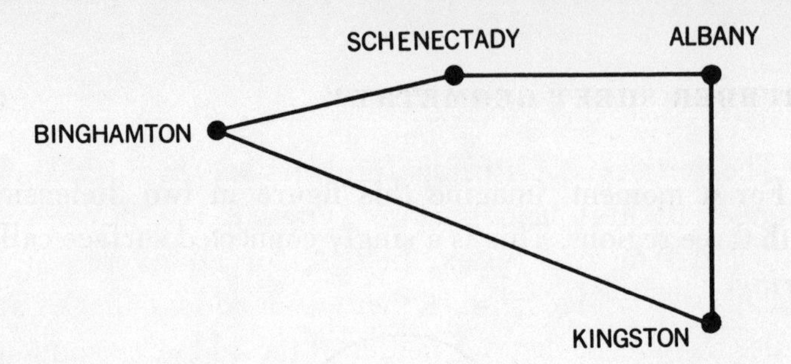

Draw the network of streets for the cluster of buildings below. The vertices, of course, are the intersections:

A New York City bridge problem:

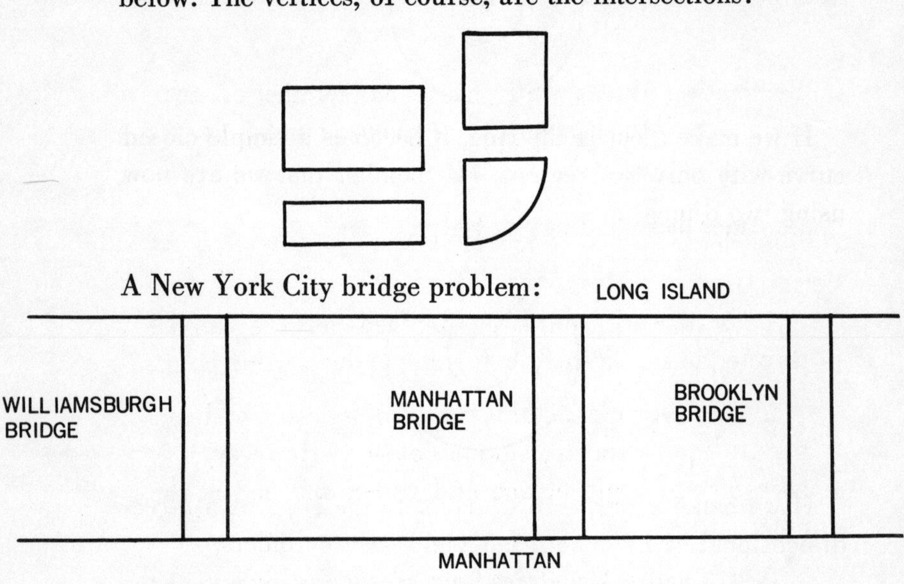

THREE-DIMENSIONAL FIGURES

Now for a look at some topological conditions in three dimensions. How would you describe the hole in this doughnut? Is it inside or outside the doughnut? Regardless of what your baker might say about putting the hole in the doughnut, a mathematician would say that the hole is outside of the doughnut. The hole is part of that region which is outside of the topological figure of a doughnut.

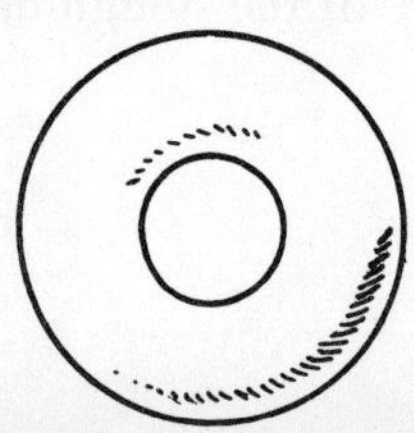

For a moment, imagine this figure in two dimensions with three regions. This is a singly connected surface called a *ring*.

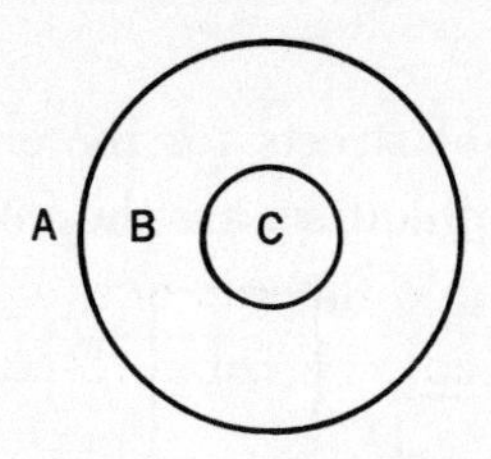

If we make a cut in the ring, it becomes a simple closed curve with only two regions. (Remember that we are now using two dimensions.)

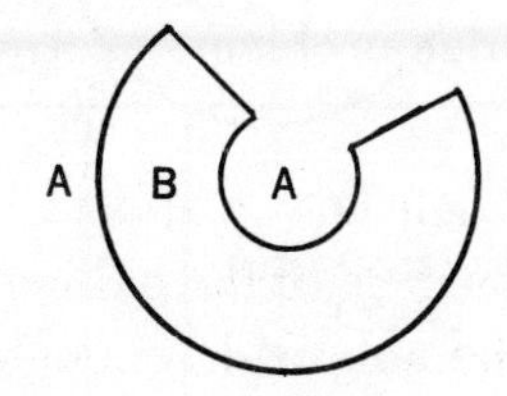

If we make a perpendicular cut to the edge of a *three*-dimensional cylinder, our cut yields two cylinders.

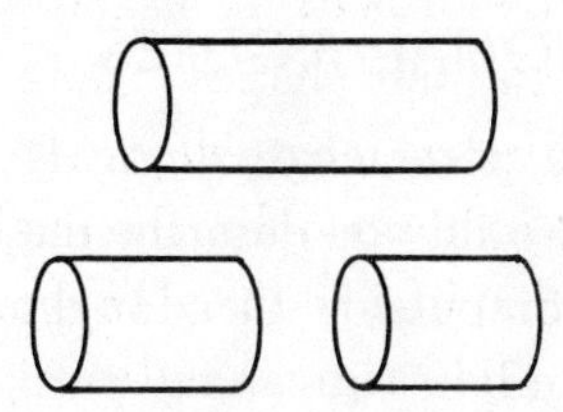

Let's return to our doughnut. Because we are dealing with three dimensions, there are only two regions, A and B, and the topological figure of the doughnut is called a *torus*.

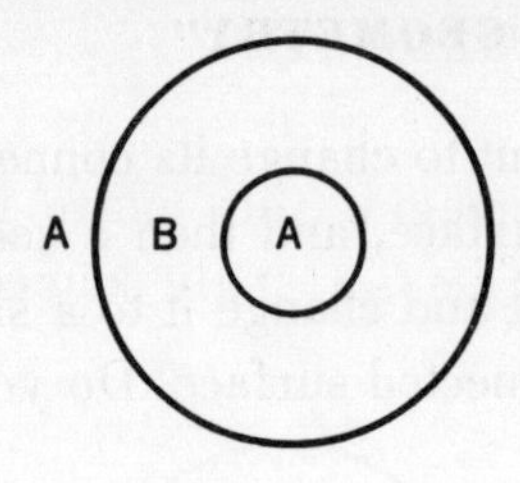

If we cut through this torus we are left with only one figure. It is now possible for this new topological figure to be distorted into a simple closed surface like a sphere.

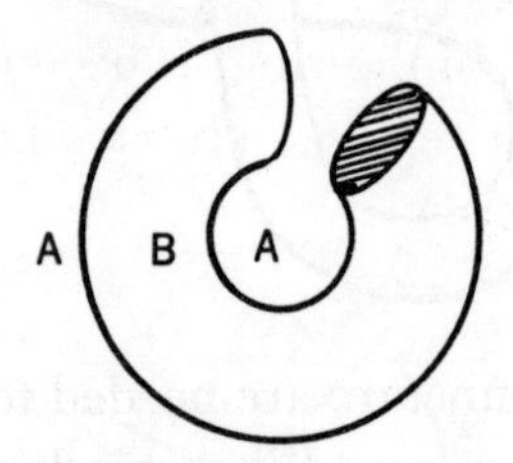

If we put a small hole into a sphere like a balloon, we could pull the entire surface of the balloon through the hole. If we could stretch the hole wide enough, we could flatten out the surface of the sphere. This could not be true of a torus or an inner tube without first making the cut shown in the illustration. We say that mathematical objects such as the sphere and the torus differ in their *connectivity*, or in the manner in which their shapes "hang together."

If we cut a cylinder lengthwise, we change the three-dimensional figure into a two-dimensional one, with the surface *equivalent* to that of a square. This surface is said to be a simple surface. The original cylinder, like a sphere, is said to have a singly connected surface.

An inner tube is said to have two surfaces and no edge.

It would take one cut to change its connectivity to that of a singly connected surface, and then a second cut, or puncture, to flatten it out and change it to a simple plane curve. Here is a *triply* connected surface. Do you know why?

Two cuts and a puncture are needed to change this figure to a simple plane curve. What kind of surfaces do the following objects have: a can of tomato juice, a fire hose, a baseball, an LP record, an ice cream cone?

Work out the problem of the electronic engineer on a doughnut, using six pins and three differently colored strings, but connect each square to each circle.

Can you draw this knot on a torus without crossing lines? You could make a clay torus, using a piece of string for a line. When you think you have made the right lines, break the torus and examine the string.

In some three-dimensional surfaces that contain edges, Euler's network formula can be easily applied. Thus, we can express topological properties in terms of mathematical equations.

In $V - A + R = 2$, substitute edges for arcs and faces for regions. Thus, in a pyramid (a regular polyhedron) $V - E + F = 5 - 8 + 5 = 2$.

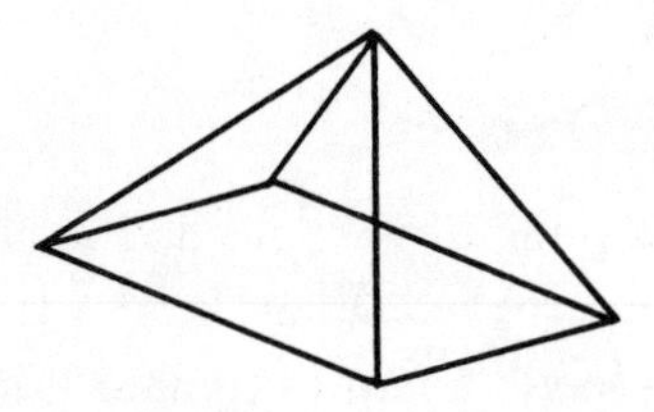

Can you apply Euler's formula to the four other regular polyhedrons: the hexahedron, octahedron, dodecahedron, and icosahedron?

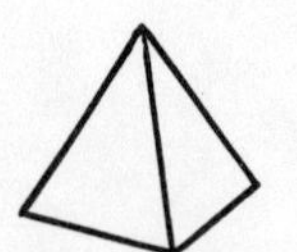

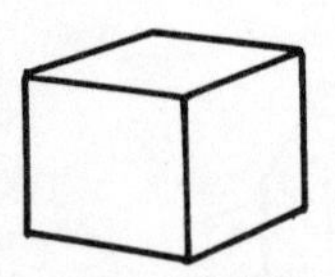

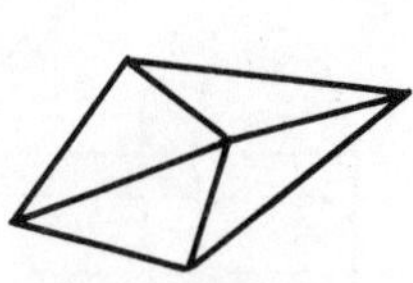

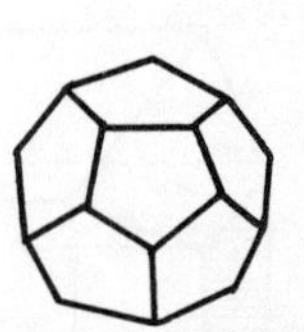

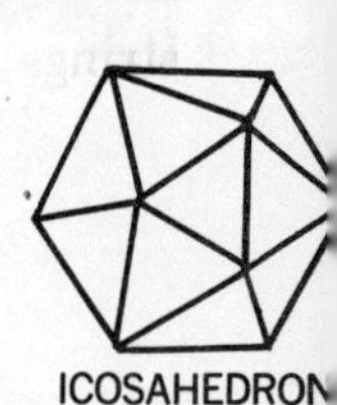

HEXAHEDRON OCTAHEDRON DODECAHEDRON ICOSAHEDRON

Can you flatten out these five regular polyhedrons to form networks? (The pyramid, for example, will look like this when flattened out.)

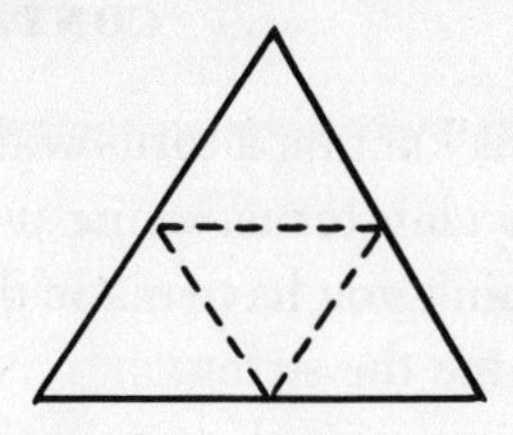

Euler's formula applies to any surface that is bounded by planes and can be distorted or deformed (without cutting or tearing) into a sphere.

$V - E + F = 2$ is the formula for those polyhedra that can be topologically transformed into spheres.

$V - E + F = 0$ is the formula for any polyhedron that can be topologically transformed (without cutting or tearing) into a torus.

Here is a hollow geometric shape that can be "blown up" into the shape of a torus. Can you show that $V - E + F = 0$?

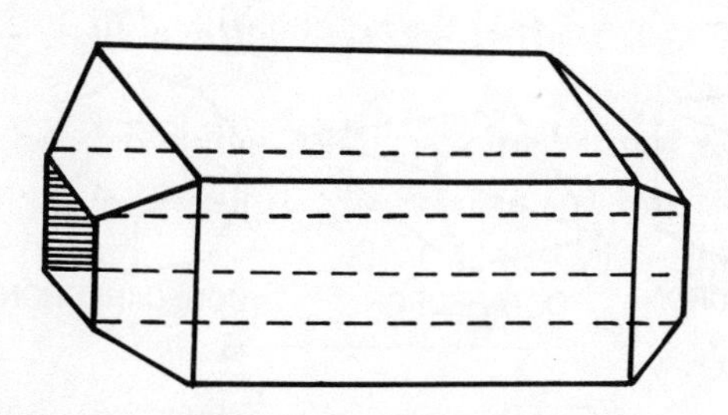

APPLICATION OF SET THEORY

The mathematics of topology is a complex study that also

involves set theory. The application of set theory to topology involves many complex axioms and theorems that are reserved for the topologist, just as statistical terms and formulas are reserved for the statistician. Nevertheless, we can use what knowledge we have of it to help us understand some basic principles.

Did you get a rubber band? Make a cut in it, then stretch it taut. Now tack it down to a suitable piece of cardboard and mark off the following points:

$$-1 \quad -\frac{1}{2} \; -\frac{1}{4} \; -\frac{1}{8} \;\; 0 \;\; +\frac{1}{8} \; +\frac{1}{4} \; +\frac{1}{2} \quad +1$$

The fractions 1/2, 1/4, and 1/8 do not refer to fractions of an inch, but to points on the line from 0 to +1, or from 0 to −1. There are also other possible points: 1/3, 1/5, 1/6, 1/7, 1/9, etc.

Each point on the line belongs to a *neighborhood*. A neighborhood consists of all the points that surround or are nearby any given point. Thus, the neighborhood of 1/2 may consist of 1/4, 1/2, 1/3. If we wanted to enlarge the neighborhood, we might say that the neighborhood of 1/2 consists of 0, 1/4, 1/2, 1/3.

Suppose we wanted to describe a neighborhood of zero. We could describe this as a set of points which included all the points from −1/4 to +1/4:

$$-\frac{1}{4} \quad 0 \quad +\frac{1}{4}$$

All the points in this set crowd in toward zero. We may

exclude some of the points of this set from the neighborhood of zero, but as long as we include some points that crowd about zero, zero is the *limit* point of the set. Call this Set A and *exclude* zero from this set. Set A includes all the points between $+1/4$ and $-1/4$, but does not include the point, zero. Because it does not include zero, we call this an *open set.*

Suppose we had a set of $1-1/3$, $0+1/3$, $1-1/4$, $0+1/4$, etc. We would have multitudes of points clustering about 0 and 1. This Set B would contain two cluster points as distinguished from Set A, which had one cluster point (called a limit point). Cluster points and limit points are also called points of *adherence.*

We have said that Set A did not contain zero, a point of adherence. Limit points and cluster points are not the only points of adherence. A point of adherence may be any point *in* the set, as well as the points *outside* the set (designated as limit or cluster points).

If we want Set A to be a closed set, we enlarge it by including zero. Set A now contains all its points of adherence and is called a closed set. Similarly, Set B can be made a closed set by including cluster points 0 and 1. The empty set is also considered a closed set, because it contains *no* points of adherence.

The law of complementation of sets holds true in topology and is very much concerned with these points of adherence. Let us assume that the complement of an open set is a closed set.

Let set B be a closed set including all points of adherence and cluster points 0 and 1. Let C be an open set. No point in set C can be included in the closed set B, nor can any point in C be a point of adherence in set B, by definition of a closed set. Every point in the open set belongs to a neighborhood that cannot be contained in the closed set.

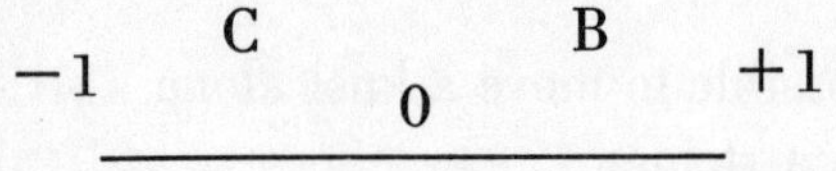

$$\underset{-1 \qquad C \qquad 0 \qquad B \qquad +1}{\rule{5cm}{0.4pt}}$$

Of course the plot thickens when we begin to apply inductive reasoning to the complement theory. We can say that since the empty set is a closed set, all the points on the line -1 to $+1$ are members of an open set. The whole line is the complement of the empty set. Conversely, because the whole line can be considered as a closed set, the empty set is an open set.

For purposes of studying topological spaces, sets on the whole line (including the empty set) may be regarded as open sets, and two rules concerning them are these:

1. The union of open sets is also an open set.
2. The set of points common to two open sets i.e., the intersection of the two sets, is an open set.

The topological structure of the whole line may be regarded as interlocking open sets.

If we joined the ends of the rubber band, we should have a closed curve that would include arcs -1 to 0 and 0 to $+1$ and all its interlocking subsets. No matter how this closed curve was then stretched, pulled, or shrunk, its topological properties would remain the same, because the conditions of the open sets remain unchanged, even though distances between points may change.

Here are two problems in topology that can be solved, but not proven. (If you want to become well known, find their proofs.)

1. It is possible to move a knot along a string. Here are two knots on a string.

As they approach each other they cannot cancel each other out, no matter how they are brought together. It is always possible to pass one knot through the other and out the other side. Can you prove why they do not cancel each other out?

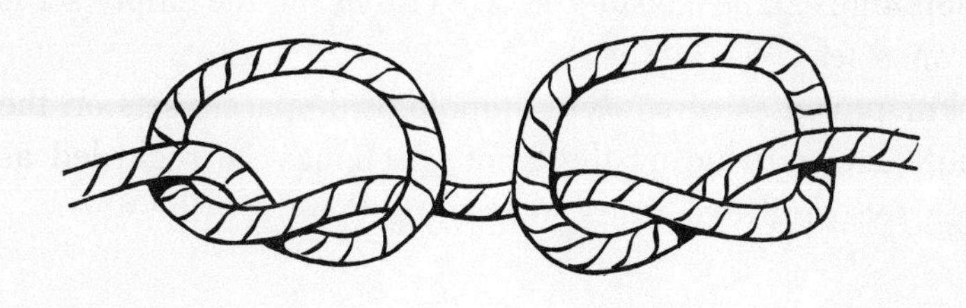

2. Perhaps the most practical problem that still needs proof is the four-color-map problem. Here is a map of a

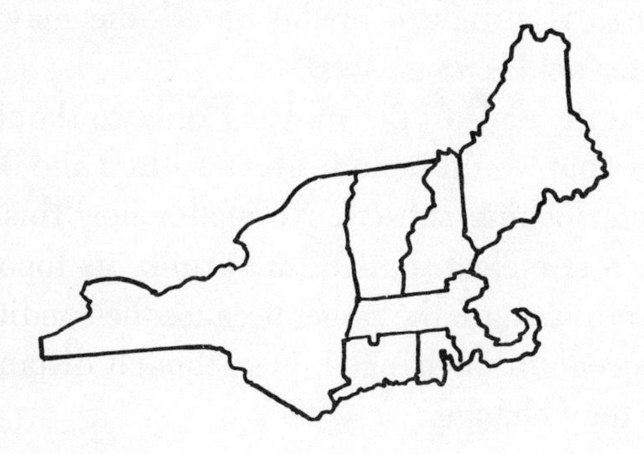

group of northeastern states. It is possible to color this or any other map by using only four colors on common borders. Of course, there are practically no straight lines in this map, but whoever heard of a straight line for a boundary between states or nations! Can you prove that only four colors are necessary, or can you draw a map that requires five different colors to distinguish its common borders?

Chapter Seven

TESTING

Appraising Test Results
What Happens to Tests After You Take Them

EVER SINCE our earliest ancestors put marks on the walls of their caves, men have tried to keep a record of their environment.

In our modern and rapidly changing world, population and information explosions provide us with a mass of data. We endlessly examine these accumulating data for averages, trends, and group characteristics that help us to learn more about our environment and ourselves.

The ancient Greeks consulted oracles to learn about future events. In a much more dependable manner, mathematics helps today's statistician — the modern oracle — to make valid and useful predictions for scientists, executives, engineers, doctors, teachers, and prospective employers.

Even more important than being a modern oracle, the statistician is something of a physician for all of society. He has a kind of mathematical stethoscope on the pulse of our contemporary world.

Some of the earliest statisticians were the Chaldean astronomers. Centuries of observation of the sun, moon, and other bodies in the universe made it possible for them to predict the changing courses of the stars across the heavens.

The universe that the modern statistician studies may not be in the sky, but something as simple as a group of ten high school students taking a test in science.

Earlier, we said that modern data were examined for averages. To learn more about this, let us see how a statistician would go about getting the average mark on a test taken by these ten boys.

He would first approach the problem by using a special symbolic notation to help him in his computations. He would call all the students in the class that are under observation a *universe*. This universe is marked X, and each student's score will be designated as X_1, X_2, X_3, and so on, up to X_{10}. When a number is written at the right bottom as X_1, it is called a *subscript*. X_N is sometimes used to designate the last item in a universe. A count of correct answers on each test paper is often referred to as a *raw* score.

RAW SCORES
98
87
66
92
76
83
89
94
78
85
848

Our statistician now totals all the individual counts, or raw scores, on the test. Let us follow him through this procedure to see how he uses symbols to do this.

The figure 848 means that the sum of the scores of all the students under consideration is 848. The average score on a test, in symbols, would be written as $\frac{\Sigma X,}{N}$ where the Greek letter Σ (sigma) indicates the sum $X_1 + X_2 + \ldots X_N$.

We know that the numerator in this test is the sum 848. The denominator is N, or in this test, 10. The average can be computed thus: $\frac{848}{10}$ or 84.8.

This kind of average is called an arithmetic *mean*. The symbol for this average, or mean, of the universe under discussion is $\bar{X}$.

This simple problem was solved by using two arithmetic operations or processes: addition and division. These operations can be arranged in the following manner:

$$\bar{X} = \frac{X_1 + X_2 + X_3 + \ldots + X_N.}{N}$$

This grouping of symbols is merely a way to give directions concerning *what* arithmetic processes should be used and *when* they should be used. It is called a *formula*. A formula is to the statistician much as a program is to a computer. A formula is simply a set of instructions.

You should be able to apply the above formula to any similar problem. $\bar{X}$ means average, N means the total number of scores, and X_N is the number of cases in the universe under discussion.

Suppose our statistician was working for an automobile manufacturer and was studying the results of scores made on a mechanical achievement test by high school boys applying for jobs with his company. Perhaps you can think of only one reason for him to do this; that is, to determine who will get the available jobs.

Actually, however, there are other reasons for examining these scores. Perhaps the mechanical achievement scores from vocational training schools were somewhat higher than the scores (for the same test) of boys who graduated from academic high schools. This would indicate, in a general way of course, that a boy's chance of success in mechanical skills would be greater if he attended a vocational school. In other words, the results of this test could show not only the individuals with the highest scores, but they would also indicate a group characteristic.

In order to determine this characteristic, the statistician might take samples of the scores from both schools. He could take a batch of tests from ten vocational schools, and another batch of tests from ten academic schools. The mean, or average, of each individual school would then be computed.

Two universes could then be compared. One universe would consist of the mean scores of each of the ten vocational schools, the other universe of the mean scores of each of the ten academic schools. X_1, for example, would now represent the mean score from one vocational school.

Let $X_1, X_2, X_3, \ldots, X_N$ represent the mean scores for each of the vocational schools and, because we have two universes, let $Y_1, Y_2, Y_3 \ldots Y_N$ represent the mean scores for each of the academic schools. Can you see how it is possible to apply the formula we gave earlier and compare the results of the mechanical aptitude tests?

$$\bar{X} = \frac{X_1 + X_2 + X_3 + \ldots + X_N}{N}$$

$$\bar{Y} = \frac{Y_1 + Y_2 + Y_3 + \ldots + Y_N}{N}$$

It is important to organize all the information properly before we can examine or process it with formulas. Sometimes this organization of data makes statistics seem as though it were a subject swamped with jaw-breaking formulas and impressive technical terms. At the bottom of all these symbols and words, however, are basic mathematical operations.

To get to the bottom of this sometimes vexing and confusing arrangement of information, let us see what happened to a recent bookkeeping test given by a large firm to hundreds of girls applying for clerical positions.

Here is a table containing a batch of 100 scores made on that test which contained 50 items, or short questions.

Table 1

50	46	41	39	38	36	33	25	18	14
50	46	41	39	38	36	33	24	18	13
49	45	41	39	37	35	31	24	18	13
48	45	41	39	37	35	29	24	17	12
48	44	40	39	37	35	29	24	16	11
48	44	40	39	37	34	29	23	16	10
47	43	40	39	36	34	28	22	16	10
46	42	40	38	36	34	28	20	16	8
46	42	40	38	36	34	26	20	15	8
46	42	39	38	36	33	25	19	15	6

Table 1 is an arrangement of a batch of 100 scores put into 10 rows and 10 columns in a descending score order from highest to lowest. Since there were only 50 items on the test, 50 is the highest possible score. No girl in this particular group made scores of 32, 30, 27, 21, 9, 7, 5, 4, 3, 2,

1, or 0. If you examine Table 1, you will find that these scores are missing.

Even by omitting those ratings which no one achieved, we still have a rather unwieldy mass of information. Let us try to organize these scores into something more compact. One of the first things a statistician would do would be to arrange each possible numerical score in descending order and place tally marks next to each score to indicate how many girls achieved that particular rating.

Table 2

SCORE	TALLIES	FREQUENCY
50	/ /	2
49	/	1
48	/ / /	3
47	/	1
46	~~/ / / /~~	5
45	/ /	2
44	/ /	2
43	/	1
42	/ / /	3
41	/ / / /	4
40	~~/ / / /~~	5
39	~~/ / / /~~ / / /	8
38	~~/ / / /~~	5
37	/ / / /	4
36	~~/ / / /~~ /	6
35	/ / /	3
34	/ / / /	4
33	/ / /	3
32		0
31	/	1

30		0
29	/ / /	3
28	/ /	2
27		0
26	/	1
25	/ /	2
24	/ / / /	4
23	/	1
22	/	1
21		0
20	/ /	2
19	/	1
18	/ / /	3
17	/	1
16	/ / / /	4
15	/ /	2
14	/	1
13	/ /	2
12	/	1
11	/	1
10	/ /	2
9		0
8	/ /	2
7		0
6	/	1
5		0
4		0
3		0
2		0
1		0
0		0
		100 Total

The number of tallies next to a score is called the *frequency* of that particular score. The arrangement of scores showing the frequency (f) of each score is called *frequency distribution.* This form of distribution of scores is still somewhat cluttered and bulky. Irregularities of distribution could be more compact and data could be handled more easily if the interval of measurement included not one score, but five scores. Here are the same scores grouped in units, or intervals, of five:

Table 3

SCORE	f
46–50	12
41–45	12
36–40	28
31–35	11
26–30	6
21–25	8
16–20	11
11–15	7
6–10	5

If we lay this table on its side, we can illustrate these scores graphically with what statisticians call a *histogram.* The left side of the table now becomes the bottom of the histogram and the frequencies become bars similar to those in a bar graph.

This histogram makes it easy to see the grouping of scores. For example: Five girls are grouped in the 6–10 interval. Seven girls scored from 11–15, and so on.

With Table 3 and the histogram we can now easily illustrate some of the language that statisticians use. Perhaps the easiest term to understand is *range* of scores, which is simply the distance from the lowest score of 6 to the highest score of 50.

The term *mode of the distribution* is used to describe that point on the scale at which more scores are found than at any other point. It is a particular characteristic, or tendency, of a group of scores that cannot be expressed by the mean.

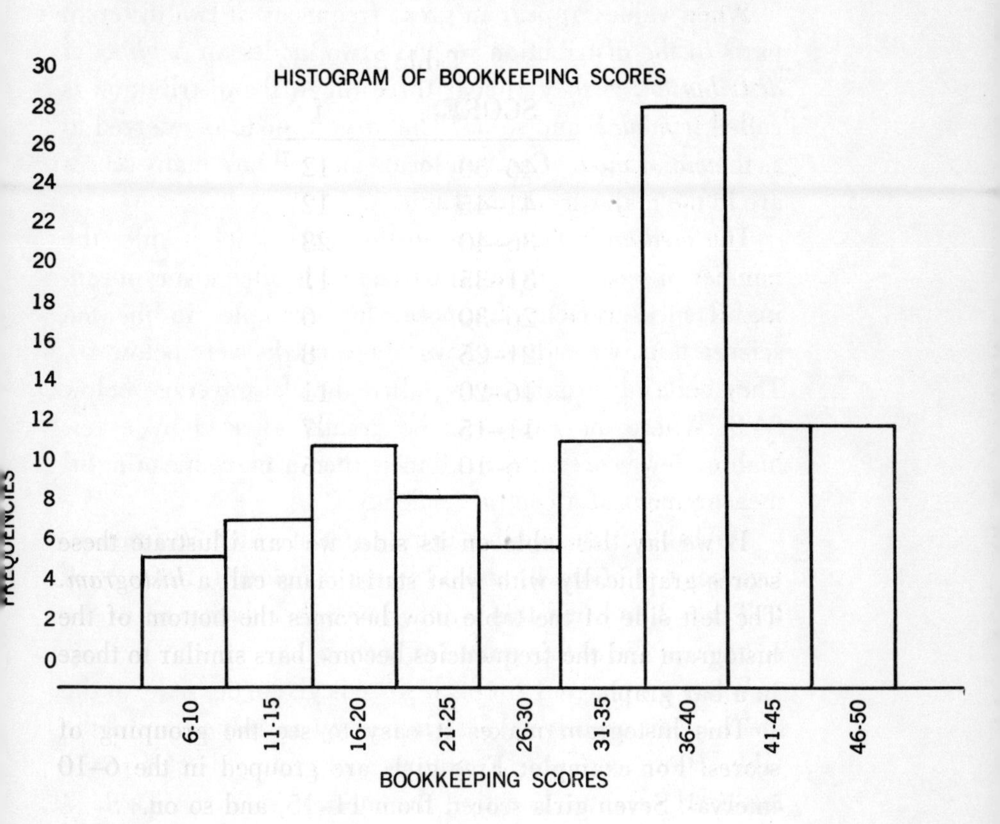

If we go back to Table 1, we can immediately see this as the score 39, which eight girls achieved. However, in a grouped distribution such as Table 3, which uses intervals of 5 scores, the true mode cannot be determined by simple inspection, but requires very difficult computations. For this reason, it is not used in every type of statistical problem. Rather, the word *mode* is used in a broader (if less accurate) sense to express any place on a scale where the frequencies occur most often.

When values appear in great frequency at two different parts of the distribution we have two modes, or a *bimodal distribution*. If they appear three times, the distribution is called *trimodal*, and so on. The largest mode is referred to as the *major mode*. Can you locate and tell how many scores are in the major mode on Table 3?

The *median* is that point on the scale which divides the number of scores into equal parts, and is often a very meaningful measurement. Suppose, for example, in the ten science tests, we had two boys whose marks were below 40. They certainly would have pulled the class average below 84.8. Where the mean can be greatly affected by a few high or low scores, the median is then a more meaningful measurement of a central tendency.

On Table 2, the median is the point at which 50 frequencies lie *at or above* it, and 50 lie *at or below* it. Refer back to Table 2 and find this point. Remember that some of the scores may lie *at* this point (or interval).

When a frequency for each score is given, the score at the median can usually be determined by an inspection of the table. However, Table 3 contains score intervals of 5 in the left-hand column. Locating the median score on Table 3 requires some computations. Refer to Table 3 and follow these computations:

1. Half of the frequencies (or half of the total number of scores) are required. Therefore:

$$\frac{N}{2} = \frac{100}{2} = 50.$$

2. Now we must count up 50 frequencies from the bottom. At the 48th frequency we are at the top of the 31–35 interval. We can say that at this interval we only need two more frequencies to make 50.

3. The interval which contains the median score is 36–40. The frequency here is 28. We must now find the median by dividing these 28 frequencies into the two points needed, or $\frac{2}{28}$, then multiplying this quotient by the distance of the interval, which is 5.

$$\frac{2}{28} \times 5 = \frac{10}{28} = 0.36$$

4. The number which is now added to the lower limit of the 36–40 step is .36. Actually, 36 is not considered the lower limit of that interval. Statisticians consider a lower limit as .5 less than the lowest number of the designated interval. Since the lowest number is 36 in the interval we are considering, the lower limit is actually 35.5 to a statistician. Add .36 to 35.5 and the answer is 35.86.

If you compared the median computed with Table 3 to the median you selected by inspection of Table 2, you would see that these comparisons are less than .2 of a point apart, which makes this method of computation quite dependable.

The median is often referred to as the 50th *percentile.* A percentile is like a rank. For example, if a score is at the 70th percentile in a batch of 1,000 scores, it ranks as good or better than 700 other scores.

The median, or any percentile point, for example the 70th percentile or the 25th percentile, is found first by dividing all the frequencies by the given percentile expressed as a fraction. For example: the 25th percentile is ¼, the 70th percentile is 7/10, and so on. Next, you must count up the frequency column as far as you can without passing the required point. Here the fractional distance into the next interval group must be determined to the point, or percentile, required. This fraction is multiplied by the size of the interval group. This answer must be added to the lower limit (always measured at .5 below the lowest number in the interval in which the median or other percentile is located). This sum, of course, is the required percentile point.

In the bookkeeping test, the mechanical achievement test, or in any other test that measures skills, aptitudes, or academic achievements, there are two things that employers and teachers, as well as statisticians, are very much concerned with — *validity* and *reliability.*

VALIDITY

An item on a test is valid if it can retrieve the information it sets out to get. For example, here is an item on a spelling test:

> To have some ________ I gave my brother
> a ________ of cake.
> Fill in the correct words: *piece peace.*

Suppose this item had been given thus:

> To have some ________ I gave my brother
> a ________ of cake.
> Fill in the correct words.

Here it would not be clear to the person taking the test just which words were wanted. In other words, the second item would not be a valid one. To be valid, a test must measure what its authors claim it measures. Validity of a test can be determined in several ways:

(a) The opinions of experts in the field.
(b) An analysis of textbooks in the field.
(c) A comparison with another test that measures the same things.

RELIABILITY

An item on a test is reliable if it can be depended upon to have a useful measure of difficulty. For example: If one item on a test given to thousands of persons was never answered wrong, it might be too easy to use. On the other hand, if it was an item that no one could answer correctly without guessing, it would be too difficult to use. In both cases it would not be a reliable item for a test. Without reliable items, a test would not consistently produce the same or nearly the same score if given over again to the same person. Without reliable items, a test has no useful measure of difficulty.

Tests must be tried out to determine their reliability. A test may be given to many persons over periods of time. These test scores are then compared by statisticians to determine whether or not the test is a dependable and consistent measuring device.

One test that has proven itself to be reliable over the years is an intelligence test given by the U. S. Army. Certainly this test has been given to millions of young men from many different backgrounds and from every part of the country.

In dealing with large batches of scores, the Army statisticians are usually not concerned with raw scores or individual scores. They deal with intervals of scores as we did on the bookkeeping tests.

Earlier, when we found $\overline{X}$, or the average score for the ten boys taking the science test, we were operating on a simple problem and used the following formula:

$$\overline{X} = \frac{X_1 + X_2 + X_3 + \ldots + X_N}{N}$$

To learn more about statistics, let us look at a sample batch of scores. We will have to compute *without* individual scores for X_1, X_2, $X_3 \ldots X_N$. We must compute $\overline{X}$ from the frequencies (f) that lie within intervals of five points each on a range from 30–99.

Table 4

SCORE INTERVAL (i)	FREQUENCY (f)	DEVIATION (d)	(f) × (d)	(f) × (d)2
95–99	1	6	6	36
90–94	2	5	10	50
85–89	4	4	16	64
80–84	7	3	21	63
75–79	9	2	18	36
70–74	14	1	14	14
65–69	20	0		
60–64	11	−1	−11	11
55–59	10	−2	−20	40
50–54	6	−3	−18	54
45–49	3	−4	−12	48
40–44	2	−5	−10	50
35–39	1	−6	− 6	36
30–34	1	−7	− 7	49

Suppose these were scores made by draftees from Broken Bow, Nebraska. Even though we do not have everyone's raw score, it is easily seen that the 91 boys from Broken Bow are not all alike. In fact, this Army test showed that their scores scattered across a whole range from 30 to 99. However, there seems to be a large group of them gathered between scores of 60 and 74. We might make a reasonably cautious guess that the average (or mean) score lies somewhere between 65 and 69. We will call this *guessed* mean M.

To help us compute the *actual* mean, we will need to

mark off deviations from the guessed mean, M. (See the third column in Table 4.) Each score interval above and below the guessed mean is called a *deviation*. The deviations above the guessed mean will be 1, 2, 3, 4, 5, 6. The deviations below the guessed mean will be −1, −2, −3, −4, −5, −6.

In working with score intervals, our answer will not be as precise as it was when we added $X_1 + X_2$, etc., but statisticians have another set of instructions that will help us get a very accurate mean. One very often used formula for finding the mean, or $\bar{X}$, is:

$$\bar{X} = M + \frac{\Sigma\,(f) \times (d)}{N}\ i\ (\text{interval}).$$

Let M be 67, or the halfway point between 65 and 69, and see how much information we can supply to this formula:

$$\bar{X} = 67 + \frac{\Sigma\,(f) \times (d)}{91}\ 5.$$

The rest is simply arithmetic; $\Sigma(f) \times (d)$ means the algebraic sum of the fourth column in Table 4 called(f)×(d.) Add up all the numbers above the 65–69 step and subtract the sum of all those below the 65–69 step:

$$\begin{array}{r} +85 \\ -84 \\ \hline +\ 1 \end{array}$$

Now: $\bar{X} = 67 + \frac{1}{91} \times 5$ or $\bar{X} = 67 + (.01 \times 5)$

$$\bar{X} = 67 + .05$$

The .05 can now be regarded as the *correction* of our original estimate of 67, and the *true mean is 67.05.*

The mean is different from the median in that it requires a contribution in size from every score. The median is influenced only slightly by unusually high or low scores.

The mean is not only one of the most important statistical measures for interpreting Army intelligence tests, it is also a device that has been used to determine the Intelligence Quotient itself.

In the public schools, the mean is sometimes used as the *norm,* or the average achievement of pupils in a given grade or at a given chronological age. Sometimes the median, or even such points as quartiles or percentiles, are used. A grade norm, for example, is the mean or average test accomplishment of pupils in a particular grade (and sometimes in a particular part of the country). An age norm is the mean or average achievement of a group designated by chronological age.

Intelligence Quotients are derived from averages or means and are expressed in the formula:

$$\text{I.Q.} = \frac{\text{M A}}{\text{C A}} \times 100.$$

Intelligence Quotients are useful in that they are one method by which a student's future progress may be estimated. Simply stated, this formula means that the Intelligence Quotient is the result of dividing the *C*hronological *A*ge into the *M*ental *A*ge and multiplying the answer by 100. If a boy 10 years old has reading, mathematical, and other measured abilities corresponding to the average 10 year old boy, the formula reads: $\frac{10}{10} = 1 \times 100$, or 100.

The abilities of the average 7-, 8-, 9-, 10-year old have been determined by various batteries of intelligence tests given in the public schools over a period of many years. If the abilities of this 10-year-old boy should correspond to those of the average 7-year-old boy, the formula would read:

$$\frac{7}{10} \times 100, \text{ or } 70.$$

If the abilities of this 10-year-old boy corresponded to those of the average 12-year-old boy, how would you express this by using the formula: I.Q. $= MA/CA \times 100$?

VARIABILITY

So far, we have been concerned with measures of a central tendency — with the average, mean, median, and mode, which are useful for general statements such as, "Most of the class got marks in the 75–80 interval." However, no one who appraises the results of learning is ever satisfied with these results alone. There are measures of *variability* that are also important to any evaluation of a test.

People are different. Just as students compare different report cards, so teachers, future employers, college registrars, the Armed Forces, all study individual variations or differences in an effort to know more about the people who come to them.

One word they use to describe these variations is *deviation* (see Table 4), and one of the measurements of deviation is called the *quartile deviation.* The quartile deviation is a measure of the deviation (or scatter), or the variability of a distribution of scores about the median. It is one half the difference between the points at the 25th (first quartile) and the 75th (third quartile) percentiles in a frequency distribution. These points are called Q_1 and Q_3, respectively.

To determine the quartile deviation, follow the same steps used in finding the median to find Q_1 and Q_3, except that $Q_1 = 1/4$ and $Q_3 = 3/4$ of the frequencies. Thus:

$$Q_1 = 1/4 \text{ of } 91$$
$$Q_3 = 3/4 \text{ of } 91.$$

The formula for finding the quartile deviation is:

$$Q = \frac{Q_3 - Q_1}{2}.$$

Can you find the quartile deviation in Table 4?

The *standard deviation* is a measure of the spread of *all* the scores. We have seen, in Table 4, that deviations are marked off from some central position. To average these deviations would seem a natural measurement to take in order to measure the average dispersion. However, we have noticed that the sum of the deviations is computed from positive and negative deviations that cancel each other out. We need a method that will account for the size of the deviation only, and will disregard the + or − distinctions.

First, we shall square the deviations. Look at the last column in Table 4. We have gotten rid of negative signs without committing algebraic murder. All deviations are squared; now we can take the mean of the squares.

This result is called the *mean square deviation.* However, it is a measure of variance as a *square* rather than a measure of variance as a linear measure. In order to change this to a linear measurement, we must take the square root using this formula: $\sigma = \sqrt{\frac{\Sigma d^2}{N}}$.

The small Greek letter sigma (σ) is the symbol used to designate the standard deviation. This measure is called the root-mean-square deviation or standard deviation for ungrouped scores (or scores not placed in intervals).

The standard deviation is one of the most vital statistical measurements, as we shall see in the next chapter. Yet, attempts to form a mental picture of this particular measure of variability are not very satisfactory. It is only by working problems through that the concept becomes clear. One visual explanation is possible, however, in a very special and so-called "normal" frequency curve.

In the illustration below, the standard deviation (S. D.) is the distance from the mean to the points of inflection, or those points on the curve at which the curve changes from one direction to another.

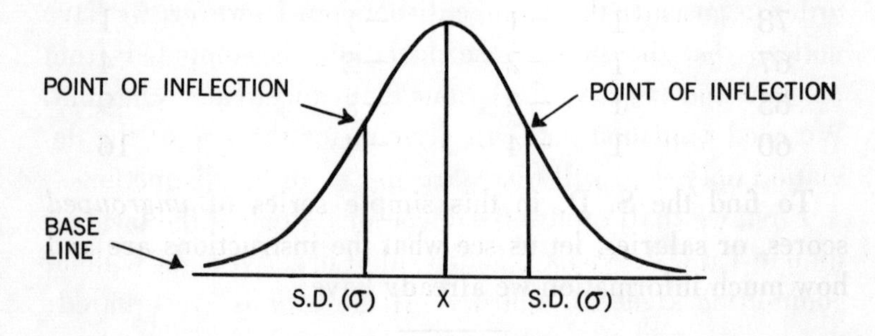

Also, this distance from the mean to one point of inflection contains 34.13 per cent of the area under the curve (in other words, 34.13 per cent of the total number of scores). Furthermore, it may be stated that 68.26 per cent of all the scores in this "normal" distribution lie not more than 1 S. D. above or below the mean ($\bar{X}$), that is, to the right or left of the mean, $\bar{X}$. This type of curve is so very special because many formulas can be applied to it.

The formula, $\sigma = \sqrt{\frac{\Sigma d^2}{N}}$, is a simple set of instructions for operating on a series of ungrouped scores. To see how it works, let us apply it to the following table which contains weekly salaries of a small printing company listed in rank (not interval) order.

Table 5

SALARY	f	d	(f) × (d)	$(f) \times (d)^2$
94	1	4	4	16
89	1	3	3	9
88	1	2	2	4
87	1	1	1	1
84	1	0		
78	1	−1	−1	1
67	1	−2	−2	4
65	1	−3	−3	9
60	1	−4	−4	16

To find the S. D. in this simple series of *ungrouped* scores, or salaries, let us see what the instructions are and how much information we already have:

$$\sigma = \sqrt{\frac{60}{9}}$$

$$\sigma = \sqrt{6.67} = 2.58.$$

(The S. D., or root mean square deviation, for Table 5 is 2.58.)

For a series of scores grouped into intervals in a frequency table, as in Table 4, the formula is somewhat more complex, where: i = interval, c = the correction (added to find the mean).

$$\sigma = i \sqrt{\frac{\Sigma f d^2}{N} - c^2}$$

Here are several problems for you to work out, using the information you already have.

1. Find the standard deviation in Table 3.

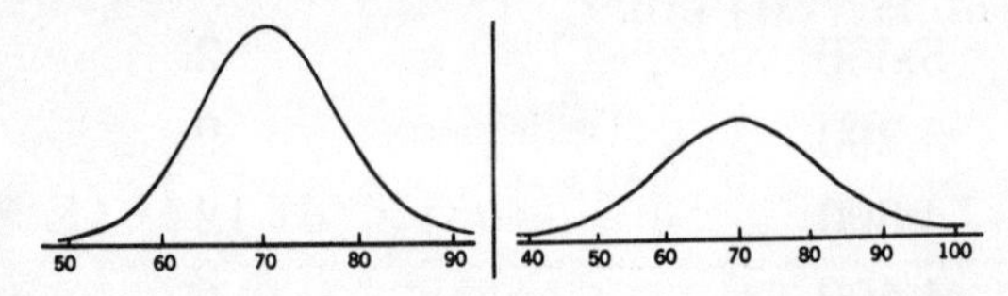

2. Compare these two normal, or bell-shaped, curves. Without doing any arithmetic, answer the following questions: Are the guessed means the same? Are the S. D.'s the same?

3. A college board exam revealed the following scores:

SCORE INTERVAL(i)	FREQUENCY(f)
95–99	3
90–94	7
85–89	13
80–84	21
75–79	34
70–74	28
65–69	17
60–64	9
55–59	4
50-54	1

If the frequencies are given in terms of hundreds, find the true mean.

4. Suppose a school board wishes to prove to a community that its teachers are well paid. The salary distribution is as follows:

$11,500	1
10,000	1
6,400	3
6,000	1
5,600	2
5,200	9
4,800	12
4,400	6

Compute the mean; the median.

Make a histogram and locate the major mode.

Questions: (a) If the board only published the mean, would this be a true measure of central tendency? (How many teachers receive the mean?)

(b) Are the median and modes any better statistics for showing the community where its top dollars are going?

(c) If you were a member of the school board, how would you publish these statistics in the most clear and honest manner?

5. Lefty Wright is a major league pitcher with the following record:

	GAMES	WON	LOST	PERCENTAGE	EARNED RUN AVERAGE
1956	11	4	7	.364	3.88
1957	22	12	10		4.00
1958	13	6	7		3.81
1959	21	11	10		4.50
1960	25	13	12		3.86
1961	18	8	10		5.81
1962	15	9	6		3.48
1963	24	15	9		3.01

Complete the column under percentage.

Find his lifetime percentage and lifetime earned run average.

Chapter Eight

PROBABILITY and STATISTICS

ROGER MARIS 12 GAMES AHEAD OF BABE RUTH'S 1927 ALL TIME RECORD . . . . MAY PASS 60 HOME RUN MARK . . . .
TOTAL ECLIPSE EXPECTED TO PASS OVER NORTHERN UNITED STATES . . . .
U. S. POPULATION TO REACH 200 MILLION BY 1967 . . . .
TRAFFIC DEATHS LIKELY TO GO OVER 600 NEW YEAR'S EVE . . . .
75 MILLION SPENT ON FLOORS LAST YEAR . . . .
NUMBER OF TV SETS TO BE INCREASED BY 20 PER CENT . . . .
3.16 INCHES RAIN FELL DURING STORM IN IOWA . . . .
COST OF LIVING UP BY .05 LAST MONTH . . . .
1,000,000 EARTHQUAKES EXPECTED IN 1964 . . . .

When we look at these headlines, we seldom stop to ask, "How do 'they' know?" We accept these dramatic statements as true, or quite likely to become true. Over recent years, the statistician has proved himself to be useful in predicting events. Not only have we accepted his predictions, we run our lives by much of what he says.

Roger Maris certainly was happy about the predictions

of the baseball statisticians, and enthusiastically went on to live up to their estimates.

The population explosion that has been predicted is even now affecting our lives through the search for untapped sources of food in such places as on the ocean floor.

The statistical estimates of high traffic fatalities are so alarming as to cause safety campaigns. In some states, drivers keep their lights on day and night during the dangerous holiday times as a symbol of concern for careful driving.

If statisticians tell us that the cost of living is rising, we try to budget our money more carefully than before. You might say that there is a high probability that statistics affect all of our lives.

To learn more about probability and statistics, let us look at those headlines again. Can you select those which contain predictions and those which contain facts? When a statistician predicts a future event, such as a population increase, he describes it in terms of a *probability*. After the census has been taken it becomes a *statistic*. Another way to understand this relationship is to say that as the study of physics is to the practical problems of engineering, so is the study of probability to practical statistical problems.

It is easy to see the close relationship between probabilities and statistics. *If* there are an average of 1,000,000 tremors and quakes per year, *then* there probably will be about 1,000,000 in 1964. *If* the population of the United States keeps increasing at the rate currently estimated by statisticians, *then* it will probably reach 200 million by 1967, and so on. This close relationship of probability to statistics, which makes modern estimates and predictions possible, is often expressed in terms such as *if . . . then*.

Of course, some people will never accept anything less than a 100 per cent certainty. Yet, statisticians can give these people at least two numbers to describe their thinking. When an "event" is certain to take place, its probability of occurrence is taken to be 1. When an "event" is impossible, it has a probability value of 0.

For the rest of us, who want to know about the national unemployment rate in relation to our own community, the cause and effect relationship of smoking to lung cancer, and other vital modern problems, the statistician must find values between these absolutes of 0 and 1. Finding these intermediate values requires the gathering and processing of statistical data.

Take another look at the beginning of this chapter. You will find the words *may, likely, expected.* These are words that do not deal with absolutes like *true* or *false.* It is not the purpose of this chapter to pour out dazzling complex formulas and jaw-breaking terminology which statisticians use to find numerical values for these intermediate measures between 0 and 1. Rather, the purpose is to illustrate, in a more general way, the manner in which a statistician goes about making a prediction, or how he helps responsible authorities in government, industry, and education to make decisions that affect all of our lives.

Let us begin with a probability that lies halfway between those cutoff points, 0 and 1 — the probability of $\frac{1}{2}$ or 0.5. In tossing a coin, when the coin lands on only a head or a tail, and not on its edge, one of two mutually exclusive events can take place. *Mutually exclusive* means that the occurrence of one event precludes the occurrence of the other: either a head or a tail will turn up. The probability of getting a head is ½ and the probability of getting a tail is also expressed as ½. A probability is always expressed as a fraction or a percentage. An *a priori* probability is one that does not depend on experiment to establish.

Each die in a pair of dice has six faces. With "honest" dice, each one of these faces is as likely to come up as another. The probability of getting one die to turn up a 5, for example, is expressed as the ratio 1/6. Do you know how the probability of *not* getting a 5 would be expressed? We would say $1 - 1/6$, or absolute certainty (1) minus the probability of getting a 5 equals the probability of *not* getting a 5. Thus: $1 - 1/6 = 5/6$.

Do you see how this might be expressed in terms of complements? If we agree that 1 makes a complete set, then 1/6 is the ones complement of 5/6, or 5/6 is the ones complement of 1/6.

If the dice are honest, it is easy to see that five other events are also possible (1, 2, 3, 4, or 6 can turn up). You can observe, in a long series of throws, that 5 will come up close to 1/6 of the time. Use this fraction as your guide:

$$\frac{\text{number of successes (numerator)}}{\text{number of trials (denominator)}}.$$

The number of trials may be regarded as the number of successes plus the number of failures.

Perhaps you have thrown the dice thirty-six times and 5 turned up nine times. This would be expressed as: $\frac{9}{36}$ or $\frac{1}{4}$. This is quite far from 1/6. Continue throwing for a total of sixty times. If the 5 turns up only three more times our ratio is $\frac{12}{60} = \frac{1}{5}$.

If you throw the dice for a total of 180 times, your ratio is more likely to approach 1/6. All we are saying here is that the greater the number of trials, the closer we are likely to come to the probability ratio of 1/6. In doing so, we have stressed the *empirical* method of finding probabilities. This method is used in many fields of research.

To learn more about the techniques of the statistician, let us learn some of the rules that affect probabilities.

The Addition Law states that the probability that at least one of two events will occur is the sum of the probabilities of each event, minus the probability of the simultaneous occurrence of both events. Let E and F be the two events, and P represent probability. Then:

$$P(E + F) = P(E) + P(F) - P(EF).$$

Example: What is the probability of at least one 3 turning up when two dice are thrown? Let E be the event of a 3 turning up on the first die, and F the event of a 3 turning up on the second die.

Then:

$$P(E + F) = \frac{1}{6} + \frac{1}{6} - \frac{1}{36} = \frac{11}{36},$$

where:

$$P(E) = \frac{1}{6}, P(F) = \frac{1}{6}, \text{ and } P(EF) = \frac{1}{36}.$$

Earlier, in tossing a coin, we said that only one of two mutually exclusive events would take place. There are other possible situations in which only one of several mutually exclusive events can take place, and there is an *Addition Law for mutually exclusive events.* This addition rule states that the probability that one of several mutually exclusive events will occur is equal to the sum of their individual probabilities.

In numbers from 0 to 1, what does this really mean? Suppose you had a pail of 400 marbles: 200 white, 100 green, and 100 orange. If we picked out one green marble, of course any other color would be excluded on that trial. What would be the probability of getting either a green *or* a white by drawing *one* marble only? Because the white marbles make up one half of the pail and the green make up one quarter, we would state this addition rule in this fashion:

Probability
(White or Green) $= P(W) + P(G)$ or $\frac{1}{2} + \frac{1}{4} = \frac{3}{4}$.

The fraction $\frac{3}{4}$ lies between 0 and 1 and expresses the probability for this event. (An event may be described as a result of a trial.)

Conditional Probabilities. The probability that an event, F, occurs on the condition that the event, E, has already occurred is denoted by $P(F|E)$, and is known as the *conditional probability* of F under the condition E. In contrast, $P(F)$ is called the *absolute probability* of F.

Multiplication Law of Probability. The probability that both of two events will occur is the product of the absolute probability of one event by the conditional probability of the other under the condition of the first event. For example:

$$P(EF) = P(E)\,P(F|E) = P(F)\quad P(E|F).$$

Illustration: Find the probability of drawing 2 white balls in succession from a pail containing 40 white balls and 60 black balls when the drawings take place without replacement. Let E be the event, "white ball on first draw" and F be the event, "white ball on second draw." Then $P(E) = 40/100 = 2/5$ and $P(F|E) = \frac{39}{99} = \frac{13}{33}$, so that

$$P(EF) = \frac{2}{5} \times \frac{13}{33} = \frac{26}{165}.$$

The Multiplication Rule of statistically independent events states that the probability that each one of several independent events will occur is equal to the product of their individual probabilities. (Events are said to be independent when they in no way affect each other.) Let us see what this means in numbers from 0 to 1.

What are the probabilities of getting a green marble on the first trial (then replacing the green marble) and a white marble on the second trial? (See pg.150)

Because the white marbles make up one half of the pail and the green marbles make up one quarter, the multiplication rule is stated like this:

Probability
(White and Green) $= P(W) \cdot P(G)$ or $\frac{1}{2} \times \frac{1}{4} = \frac{1}{8}$.

The fraction $\frac{1}{8}$ lies between 0 and 1 and expresses the probability for this event.

Suppose we are tossing dice. Can you write the ratio or fraction that expresses the probability that two 5's will turn up? Since we are dealing with two dice and want the probability of a 5 on each *die*, we compute this by the *multiplication rule:* $1/6 \times 1/6 = 1/36$.

Let us take this newly discovered knowledge on to greater things. In a single coin toss (of an ideal coin) only two events are possible: a head or a tail. Earlier we said that the probability of getting a head is one half and the probability of getting a tail is also one half.

Do you remember the graphs we made based on frequency distributions of bookkeeping scores? The graph below shows a probability distribution for the events that can result from a toss of an ideal coin.

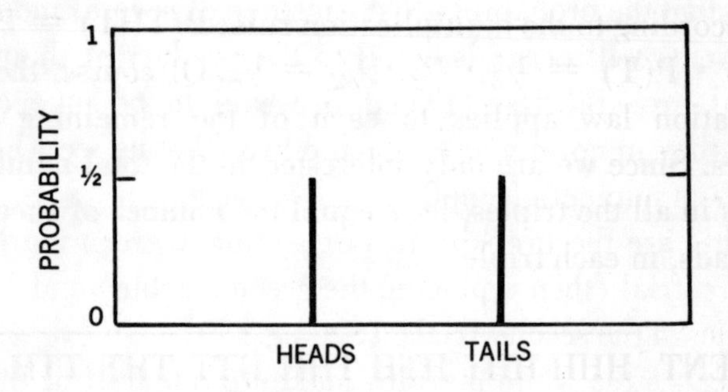

It is now possible to represent probability distribution by graphs as well as by formulas.

If we are dealing with sets of events and each one of these events consists of two mutually exclusive outcomes, we say we are dealing with a *binomial* distribution, or the distribution of a quantity consisting of *two* alternative outcomes. Two events are mutually exclusive if one event precludes the other (a coin turning up a head cannot at the same time turn up a tail).

Try writing out the eight possible combinations for tossing a coin three times. If you do you will be describing a binomial distribution. Suppose we are interested in the number of heads we get. The possible outcomes in order of the number of heads to a triple are:

HHH, HHT, HTH, THH, HTT, THT, TTH, TTT.

Instead of considering each toss as a trial, consider a triple toss as *one* trial. Let the result of this trial be the event for which we wish to compute a probability (of occurrence). What is the probability of success for any triple such as THT?

According to the multiplication rule: $P(THT) = P(T) \cdot P(H) \cdot P(T) = \frac{1}{2} \cdot \frac{1}{2} \cdot \frac{1}{2} = \frac{1}{8}$. Of course, the multiplication law applies to each of the remaining seven triples. Since we are only interested in the total number of *heads* in all the triples, let x equal the number of successes, or heads, in each triple.

EVENT	HHH	HHT	HTH	THH	HTT	THT	TTH	TTT
x	3	2	2	2	1	1	1	0

Although x takes on different values, each triple has a probability of $\frac{1}{8}$. Consider the probabilities of getting two heads in a triple. Do you remember the addition rule? As in the addition rule, we are dealing with each triple as a mutually exclusive event. Let P(2) represent the probability of success in a triple (i.e., two heads in a triple):

$$P(2) = P(HHT) + P(HTH) + P(THH) = \frac{1}{8} + \frac{1}{8} + \frac{1}{8} = \frac{3}{8}.$$

The probability of success for any triple is $\frac{1}{8}$, and $\frac{3}{8}$ is the probability of getting any one of the three triples that have two heads and one tail.

So far, with dice, coins, and marbles, we have been dealing with *discrete variables,* or variables that can be counted and given a whole number. For example, one white marble, two sides on a coin, two ones or two fives by tossing dice are discrete variables.

We have described the probability of these counted events as a binomial distribution, where x was given different numerical values. Discrete variables can also be such things as the number of children in a family or the number of automobiles sold in a day.

There is another type of variable that cannot be counted, but must be *measured* and rounded off to the nearest desired decimal. Measurements of rainfall, temperatures, weights, and heights are such examples, and are called *continuous variables,* where x may take on values over a range.

Suppose scientists were making temperature studies about some point on the earth's surface. The following histogram shows a year's recorded observations. (In order to keep the histogram perfectly balanced on both sides, intervals 0–10 and 91–100 contain only 2.5 days each.)

Certainly the bell-shaped curve imposed upon the histogram has a symmetrical shape. We saw this bell-shaped curve earlier. It is one widely occurring phenomenon most

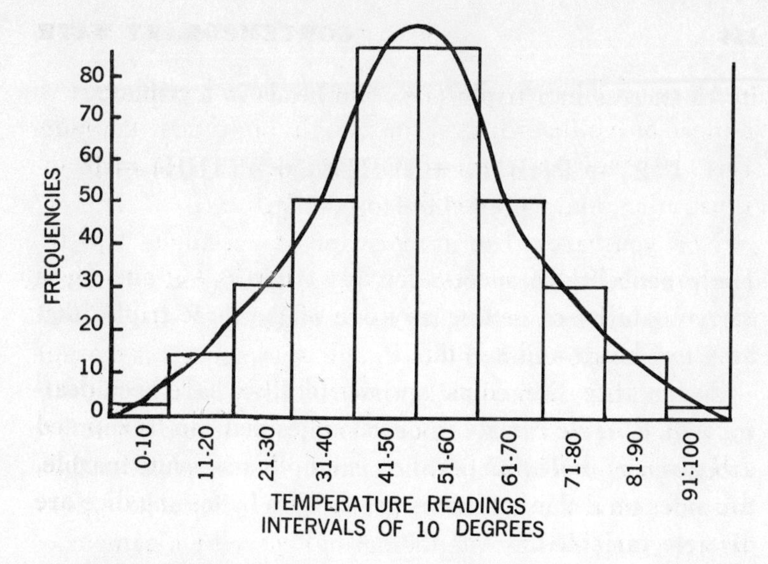

fundamentally important to statistics. It is called a *normal distribution curve.*

If we were to make a histogram based on the heights of all the soldiers at Fort Benning, Georgia, or of the distances from a bull's-eye made by a naval gunnery class, or of the lengths of rats' tails, we would come up with something to which we could "fit" the normal distribution curve.

Here is a game you can construct that will help you to understand the normal distribution curve:

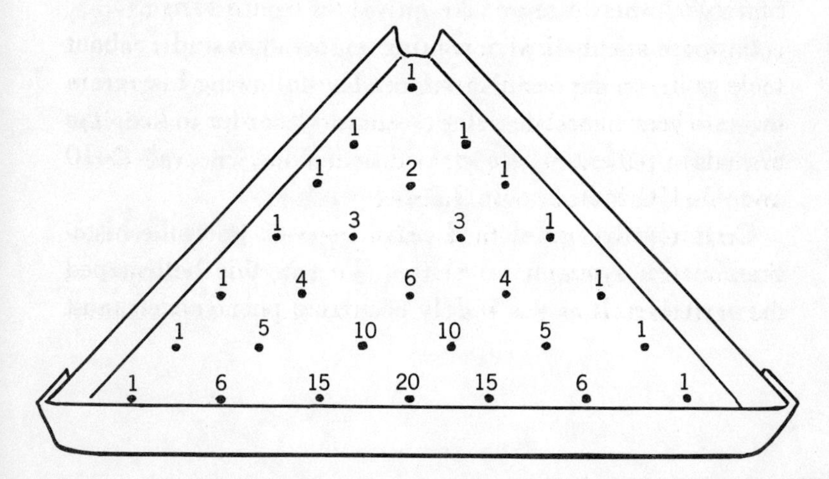

Mark off these numbers, as shown, about 1 inch apart on a piece of cardboard. Push in straight pins under the numbers. Fold up the edges of the cardboard as shown in the illustration, and cut open the top corner.

Now you have a box in the shape of a triangle. This triangle actually has a name. It is called Pascal's triangle, after the seventeenth century mathematician, Blaise Pascal.

A quick inspection of the triangle shows that 2 is the sum of the numbers immediately above it; likewise, 3 is the sum of $1 + 2$, seen directly above the 3, and so on. There are other concepts related to this triangle that help statisticians to understand the nature of probabilities, but at this point we are going to illustrate the normal curve by a game.

Place a book under the top of your cardboard version of Pascal's triangle. If you drop a marble or several marbles through the hole at the top, you are, in effect, simulating a pinball game. In several hundred tries, and without "tilting" Pascal's triangle, see how many events occur in the center and how many occur near the sides. A large number of trials and events should convince you that you are approaching the normal distribution curve.

Plotting the normal distribution curve accurately, or "fitting" it to a histogram, requires the application of very complex mathematical formulas. However, we can take a look at some important areas under the normal curve in order to learn more about the techniques used by statisticians to make predictions, assist in decision-making, and determine the quality of manufactured products.

First, let us begin with the histogram itself. The vertical line, or axis, contains f (the frequencies). We will refer to the vertical axis as the Y axis. The horizontal axis contains the continuous temperature changes from 0 to 100. We will call this the X axis.

The mean, which we will now designate as μ, is measured along the X axis from 0 to the highest point of the curve. The multiples of the *standard deviation* are marked off on the X scale. The *point of inflection* of a curve is a point at which the curvature changes. The area under the normal distribution curve within 1 standard deviation of the mean amounts to 68.26 per cent of the total area.

A perpendicular line drawn from the X axis to the curve is called an *ordinate* of the curve. The line at μ is drawn perpendicular from the mean to the highest point of the curve. It is called the *highest ordinate.* $\bar{X}$ and μ can be used to denote a mean and we shall examine the difference very shortly.

Since we are now considering the areas under various parts of the normal curve as measures of probability, the

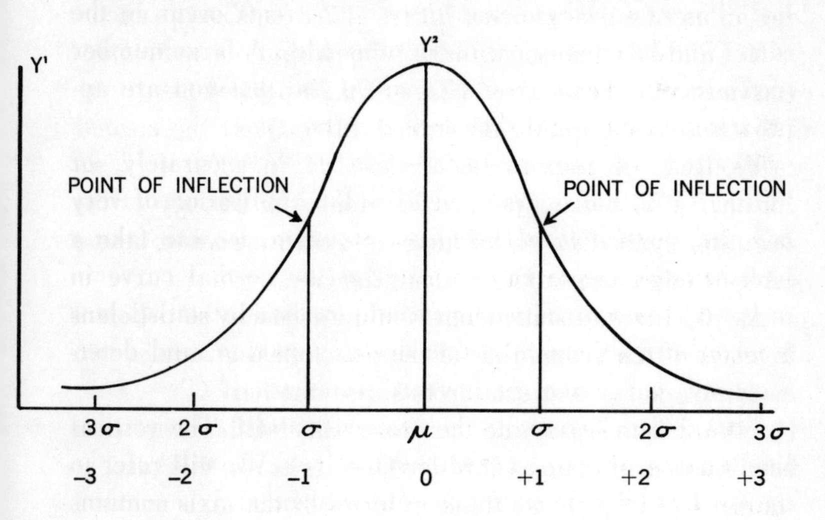

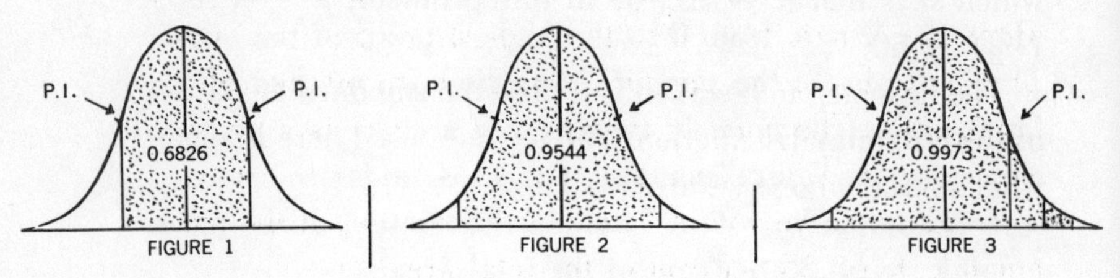

P.I. REFERS TO POINT OF INFLECTION

total area under the curve is 1. In Figure 1, the area between the highest ordinate and 1 standard deviation is .3413. The probabilities indicated by the shaded area in Figure 1 are found 1 standard deviation on each side of the mean, and are therefore equal to $2 \cdot (.3413)$, or .6826, or about 68.26 per cent.

In Figure 2, the probabilities lying within 2 standard deviations of the mean are $.4772 + .4772 = 95.44$ per cent.

In Figure 3, the probabilities lying within 3 standard deviations of the mean are .9973, or 99.73 per cent.

To learn more about the probabilities under the normal curve, let us go back to the coin toss. If, in 100 tosses, we got nearly 50 heads, we need not doubt the honesty of the coin. However, if we got 65 heads and 35 tails, we would be forced to do some thinking about the coin.

As you know, a statistician would approach the problem in terms of the probability of the occurrence of one of two mutually exclusive events, in this case one half ($P = \frac{1}{2}$). He would then determine the probability of the event of a head's not turning up as Q where $Q = 1-P$. In this case, of course, $Q = \frac{1}{2}$. If we think in terms of the area under a normal curve involved in tossing a coin 100 times, the range is 100 tosses. The mean is determined by a formula which says that $\mu = nP$, or in this problem, $\mu = (100)(\frac{1}{2}) = 50$.

The next step to be taken is to find the standard deviation of the binomial distribution. The formula used here is somewhat similar to one we already know.

$$\sigma = \sqrt{nPQ}$$

$$\sigma = \sqrt{100 \times \tfrac{1}{2} \times \tfrac{1}{2}} = \sqrt{25} = 5.$$

To find the probability of 65 heads turning up in 100 tosses, we must find the exact corresponding area under the curve.

We have learned that the X scale is laid off in units of the particular distribution we wish to represent, in this case the tosses of a coin. In order to have a scale that will represent *any* point on a normal distribution curve in terms of a probability, we must create a new horizontal scale, the Z scale.

On the Z scale, the standard deviations to the left of the μ are expressed in minus terms, and those to the right of μ in plus terms. It is also possible to find points on the Z scale that lie between the standard deviations. There is a formula that will find the point on the Z scale that will tell us what the probability is of getting 65 heads or more in 100 tosses.

$$Z = \frac{X - \mu}{\sigma}.$$

(Z equals the difference between any unit of X and the mean, divided by the standard deviation.)

X is the point on the X scale that represents 65 heads. A statistician would not compute using 65. He would take the next lowest number, 64.5. He would then be able to think of 65 tosses as lying in an area to the right of 64.5 on the X scale. We have computed σ as 5 and μ as 50. Now,

$$Z = \frac{64.5 - 50}{5} = \frac{14.5}{5}$$

$$Z = 2.9$$

Look up Z = 2.9 in the Table, Areas Under the Normal Probability Curve, and the answer is .4981. This must be subtracted from

$$P = \frac{1}{2}$$

$$\begin{array}{rr} & .5000 \\ \text{or:} & -\ \underline{.4981} \\ & .0019 \end{array}$$

If a coin is tossed 100 times, the probability of obtaining 65 or more heads is 0.0019, which is definitely not a high probability.

A gas station has two pumps, A and B. Each pump contains exactly the same type of gasoline. If the attendant services 800 customers per week and "randomly" selects pump A or B in the course of his servicing, what are the probabilities that pump A will be used 550 times? Can you relate this to the last problem of the two mutually exclusive events of a coin toss? Think of a customer using only one pump at a time and that pumps A and B are now being substituted for a head or a tail in a coin toss.

SAMPLING

Anyone who has quietly licked his fingers after putting them into mother's cake icing has had a personal experience with probabilities. If that mouthful of icing tasted good, it was a sample of what would probably be a good cake. A handful of corn from a bin, a piece of cloth cut from a bolt, a sip of lemonade are all samples.

When we sampled the icing, we were really looking for information. What does it taste like? A statistician also employs sampling techniques to get information. He may take samples that will give him information about people, animals, crops, manufactured products, heat, the sun's radiation, and possibly even samples of life on another planet.

When we sampled the icing, we knew how *all* of the icing would probably taste. When a statistician takes samples, he is able to determine what the entire *population* is probably like.

The term *population* is a very important concept in sampling. It represents the total number of objects with which we are dealing. It is the universe of things under discussion. A population can mean all of the people in Bryant, Texas, or all of the unsheared sheep in Cheyenne, Wyoming. Populations do not always include people or animals. A population can also include all of the tubeless tires sold on Washington's Birthday, or all of the white sailor hats on the U. S. S. *Enterprise*. Populations like these are *finite;* that is to say they contain a definite number of objects.

An *infinite* population, on the other hand, is made up of an indefinitely large number of objects. An example of an infinite population would be the number of points within a circle.

A census is concerned with information about every member of a finite population. If we could collect information by making observations on every single object in a population and make no errors in our computations, our results would be precise. Precise results are unlikely, especially with large populations. Furthermore, census taking is bulky, time consuming, and expensive, and in the case of the points within a circle, downright impossible.

Suppose you were a manufacturer of caps for cap pistols. You couldn't observe the popping of all your powdered population. It would be impractical. In order to be "reasonably" sure that the caps will pop, you could take a *random sample* of a few hundred caps and possibly hire a few small boys with toy pistols to try them out.

The important thing to do, of course, is to take this sample at *random*. Every cap should have the same chance of being selected in the sample. If 199 caps out of 200 popped, your best estimate is that 99.5 per cent of your product was in satisfactory working order.

To improve our sampling, we might use a more refined technique. Suppose we were sampling baseball gloves. We could easily separate the population into first basemen's gloves, fielders' gloves, and catchers' mitts. This process is known as *stratification*.

There are many ways in which a statistician can select his samples. One of the most common is *systematic sampling*. For example, if he wanted to inspect the bottles of corn syrup passing by on a conveyor belt, he would perhaps begin with the second bottle and select every third bottle thereafter. A better (more random) procedure would be to mark three slips of paper 1, 2, and 3, stir them up in a box, and draw one out without looking at it. The number drawn would determine the start — first, second, or third bottle. This kind of sampling is called patterned, serial, or chain sampling. This sampling technique can be applied to a specific problem.

Every day millions of dollars worth of various products are bought by industry and government. Many of these goods are inspected by sampling techniques to give a measure of assurance that they live up to standards set by industries and government. Levels are set for accepting or rejecting these products. These levels are often computed on the Z scale. To see how this works, let us look at the following example.

The XYZ Electric Company manufactures light bulbs. This manufacturer wants to be reasonably certain that each bulb will last at least 1,000 hours. Of course the manufacturer can't "life test" every bulb, or the company would go out of business. The company hires a statistician who will determine the average life of its light bulbs.

The first thing the statistician will do is take a sample of the bulb population. Sampling a population gives more time to study the many aspects of the sample. Compared with census taking, sampling is an easier way of getting information on a small scale.

As the statistician starts to work for the XYZ Electric Company, the following are the procedures he might adopt:

1. State the purpose of the study.
2. Define the population.
3. Describe the nature of the information desired.
4. Determine the type and design of the sample to be selected.

5. Select the sample.

6. Observe, count, measure, and compute various statistical measures (mean, standard deviation, etc.).

7. State the degree of precision involved in the estimates or other results of the study and their reliability.

Let us see how he applies these procedures to sampling the bulbs.

1. The purpose of the study, stated in a general way, is simply that the manufacturer wants to produce good quality bulbs to keep up with the standards set by the industry of light bulb manufacturers. It is a *quality control* study that will determine whether or not these light bulbs will last at least 1,000 hours.

2. The population is all of the light bulbs produced by the electric company.

3. The information desired is, specifically, *what is the average life of the electric company's light bulbs?*

4. Let the sample be a random sample of 100 light bulbs of specified power and voltage rating as well as other defining characteristics.

5. Select sample batches of 100 light bulbs and test their life span.

6. On the basis of his knowledge of specifications and his experience, the company engineer formulates the hypothesis that the electric company's light bulb will last on the average 1,000 hours. Using our sample batches of 100 light bulbs each, the statistician must compute and interpret the data from the samples to determine whether or not these bulbs do meet the industry standards and the degree of confidence he may attach to his results. He will infer from

his calculations whether the population mean is really 1,000 hours. In other words, he will test the hypothesis of the engineer.

To test this hypothesis, he selects a sample of 100 bulbs, perhaps by the systematic sampling technique. In testing this sample, he gets a mean of 1,048 hours, and he designates this as: $\bar{x} = 1048$. ($\bar{x}$ refers to a sample mean.) The engineer gave him a hypothetical population mean of 1,000 hours which he designates as $\mu = 1000$. So far, so good. It appears that the bulbs are going to last longer than expected.

However, the statistician's work does not end here. He must compute his findings to a higher degree of precision so that he can make more useful inferences than merely that "the bulbs are better than expected." To do this he must integrate into his computations a concept called *standard error*. A standard error derives from the fact that any sampling distribution (such as 100 light bulbs) gives probabilities for various degrees of error that can occur in the sampling process. We may think of a standard error as the standard deviation divided by the square root of the size of the sample, or $\frac{\sigma}{\sqrt{n}}$. If the standard deviation is found to be 160, supply the known facts to this formula:

$$Z = \frac{\bar{x} - \mu}{\frac{\sigma}{\sqrt{n}}} \quad (\bar{x} - \mu = 48 \text{ hours.})$$

$\sigma = 160$, $n = 100$ we have that $Z = \frac{48}{16} = 3$

What we have done is to find the Z scale value to express the number of standard errors beyond μ.

7. The statistician would now be able to state the degree

to which these bulbs were better than expected. In fact, he would probably say that because of these 3 standard errors he rejected the engineer's hypothesis of 1,000 hours. On the basis of this sample mean of 1,048, the statistician would say that the true population mean (μ) is probably greater than 1,000 hours. In fact, if he didn't sample further, 1,048 would be the best estimate of μ.

DRAWING INFERENCES

Using testing techniques and applying probabilities to draw inferences is really getting into statistics. Suppose the Internal Revenue Department wanted to know the average mean family income in a suburb like Levittown, New York, and it wanted to have odds of 19 to 1 (or a probability of .95) that this estimate would be within $50 of the mean.

Instead of taking a lengthy and costly census, a government statistician takes a batch of 400 residents as a sample and computes a sample mean of $4,298 and a standard deviation of $500. The statistician does not know the average mean salary for the entire population of Levittown. Let us assume that in this case the sample is a large one. He will infer that because the sample is so large the mean will lie within 2 standard errors of the Levittown average, or 95.44 per cent of the mean of the entire population.

Confidence Interval

Look up the area corresponding to a Z-scale reading of 2 on the table, Areas Under the Normal Probability Curve, and find .4772. This is exactly half of .9544. The statistician will infer that the probability must be .9544 that the true mean does not differ by more than $\pm 2 \frac{\sigma}{\sqrt{n}}$ (two standard errors from the sample mean). ($\pm$ should be read as plus or minus.) Furthermore, the interval formed by adding 2 standard errors to $\bar{x}$ and subtracting 2 standards errors from $\bar{x}$ has a .9544 probability of including the population mean. This interval is called a *confidence interval.* It is another way of saying that the probability is .9544 that the population mean will fall within 2 standard errors of $\bar{x}$, or the Levittown sample average. The formula for this particular confidence interval may be written as:

$\bar{x} \pm 2 \frac{\sigma}{\sqrt{n}}.$

The 95.44 per cent confidence interval constructed for

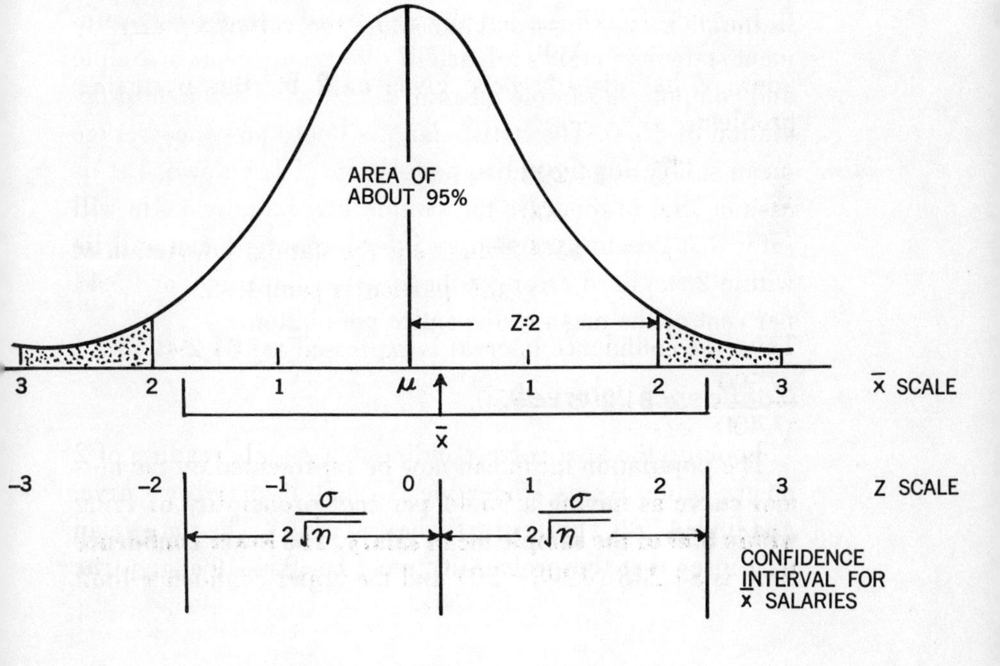

this sample mean has two halves, each 2 $\times \frac{\sigma}{\sqrt{n}}$ long. A bracket of the same size could be constructed for every value of $\bar{x}$. Can you see that if $\bar{x}$ is larger than μ it moves to the right and if it is smaller it moves to the left? Sample means lying in a range of $\bar{x} \pm 2\frac{\sigma}{\sqrt{n}}$ will include μ. Thus, 95.44 per cent of all sample means must lie within this range. For this reason, the probability is .9544 that $\bar{x} \pm 2\frac{\sigma}{\sqrt{n}}$ includes the population mean family income (μ) of Levittown.

Let us stay with this problem to learn more about plotting this confidence interval. After selecting the sample of 400 incomes, we said that the statistician found a mean of \$4,298, with a standard deviation of \$500. Let us use the formula: $\bar{x} \pm Z\frac{s}{\sqrt{n}}$ and substitute the values we already know. Z has already been given as 2 for this particular problem.

$\bar{x}$ = \$4,298
n = 400
s = \$500, where s is the standard deviation of this particular sample.

Thus, the confidence interval is expressed as: $\$4,298 \pm 2 \cdot \frac{500}{\sqrt{400}}$, or \$4,298 ± \$50.

The population mean can now be represented on the normal curve as having a 95.44 per cent probability of lying **within \$50 of the sample mean salary. The lower confidence** limit is \$4,248 (4298 − 50) and the upper confidence limit is \$4,348 (4298 + 50).

Perhaps a more costly study would have been able to locate the mean within \$10 or might have given odds as high as 99 to 1.

Although governments, as well as business and industry, are interested in economy, we should remember that they will ask at least two important things of a statistician:

1. A degree of precision. (In the preceding example this meant an estimate within \$50.)
2. A confidence interval. (In the preceding example odds of about 19 to 1 or a reliability of 95%.)

Can you make a normal curve with x and Z scales for the following problem?

Record sales are at an all-time high, and the musicians' union wants to raise the scales (wages) paid for recording sessions. Like everyone else, musicians would like to improve their living standards. In order to bargain for these higher wages, the union first conducts a survey to estimate the average dollar profits before taxes from the previous year's earnings of recording companies. The research division of the musicians' union makes a list of all the recording firms and makes a sample of 150 companies. They find that the sample mean $\bar{x} = \$14{,}989$, and the standard deviation of the sample is $s = \$4{,}685$. The union asks for a 95.44 per cent confidence interval to estimate the mean profit (μ) of all the firms in the recording industry.

Can you substitute the appropriate values for $\bar{x} \pm Z \cdot \frac{s}{\sqrt{n}}$? You must refer to the table, Areas Under the Normal Probability Curve to find the corresponding Z-scale number.

Can you complete this table?

ODDS	PROBABILITY	Z SCALE
9–1	.90	——
19–1	——	1.96
——	.98	2.33
99–1	——	——

Chapter Nine

SPACE NAVIGATION

"WHERE AM I?" is a question that mathematics has been answering for restless adventurers down through the centuries. With today's space exploration and the tremendously high speeds involved, the old question takes on a new urgency. Indeed, the answer must be almost instantaneous, because in the few moments spent in computing one's position, the space ship could have traveled perhaps 1,000 miles.

Inertial guidance systems, computers, gyroscopes, telescopes, and electronically recorded navigational tables seem to have automated the job of space navigation. Nevertheless, spacemen must understand the basic mathematical concepts underlying the design of their equipment.

The Latin word *navigare* means to conduct a ship. In a sense this means guiding a ship out from her moorings, across the seas, and safely into port again. This task is performed by the navigator of the ship. Some navigators get assistance in conducting their ships — a pilot, familiar with local waters, conducts an ocean liner through the channels, past the reefs and swift currents, and helps her reach the open seas safely, where the ship's navigator takes over. Likewise, the pilot guides the ship safely back to dock or anchorage when her voyage is over.

In "conducting" a space ship, the navigator and pilot must be concerned with departure (escape velocity), return (re-entry into the atmosphere), radiation belts, gravitational force, and the possibility of ducking a few asteroids. In addition to this, the navigator of a space craft must answer the same two questions that navigators have answered for nearly three thousand years: "Where are we?" and "How do we get to our destination?"

Ancient armies, like that of Alexander the Great, crossed great distances on land by correctly answering these questions. Columbus and other great navigators traveled over strange waters. Pioneers like Lindbergh navigated accurately through the skies where none had gone before. Just as surely as these men found their way over untraveled courses with the helping hand of mathematics, so will other men, probably in our own time, find their way across space to our earth's sister planets in the Solar System.

Yet, the space navigator might have one advantage over Alexander the Great, Columbus, and Lindbergh. He may be able to see his destination.

Let us try a simple problem wherein your vision is partially unrestricted. Suppose you went on a trip to Maine. Perhaps, along the coastline around Hancock Point, you unearthed an old pirate treasure map. (This wouldn't be a wild dream, because the United States Navy once beached several pirate ships on the Maine coast, and at least one local inhabitant recently found pirate treasure in old coins.) Suppose your map says that the treasure is buried under a blueberry patch 85 yards from a large rock which stands just on the edge of Hancock Point, and 75 yards from a well behind a fisherman's cottage. Certainly you could find the rock, and with some brush beating you could find the abandoned well.

Now, if you draw two circles, one around the rock with a radius of 85 yards, and one around the well with a radius of 75 yards, one of the points at which they intersect would tell you where the treasure is. Since one of these points lies in the ocean, it could not be, nor ever has been, a blueberry patch. This point must be disregarded.

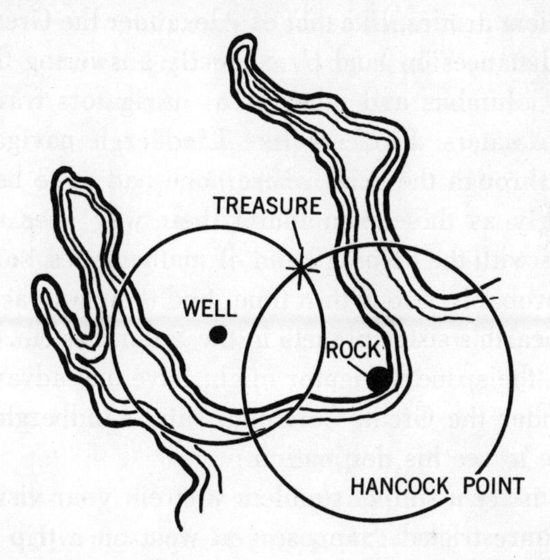

Do you see how we have answered one of the navigator's questions, "Where are we?" (or, in this case, *"Where is it?"*) The answer to "How do we get there?" is, of course, "With a shovel."

Many times an out-of-town visitor comes to the big city and gets lost in the networks of streets and thoroughfares. Suppose a relative from Kansas were coming into St. Louis, Missouri, to visit his cousin and lost his way after getting into downtown traffic. If he could find a telephone, the conversation might go something like this: "Cousin, I'm at the intersection of 12th Street and Market. How do I get to you?"

Since cousin knows the answer to the question. "Where am I?" (at 12th and Market), he can begin to answer the second question, "How do I get there?" He can now give the relative a set of instructions, or directions, to lead him to his destination.

Intersections of circles drawn on the surface of the earth help navigators much as the intersection of streets help visiting relatives. These circles help navigators to state their position and are called *earth co-ordinates.*

We can use a small rubber ball to learn more about these earth co-ordinates. Most rubber balls used for catch, stoop ball, or stick ball are made of two rubber cups connected together at their edges. Draw a heavy penciled line over this connection and call it the equator. The equator is an imaginary circle around the earth midway between the poles. It is called 0° latitude.

On one side of the ball, place the end of a string perpendicular to this line and draw it over the top of the ball until it touches the equator again on the opposite side of the ball. Place a dot at the point on this string that is exactly halfway across the top of the ball. This will represent the North Pole. Do the same thing to locate the South Pole. Next, draw a circle around the ball from pole to pole.

The distance from the equator to either pole is 90°. You can prove this by placing on the ball the straight edge of a protractor held perpendicular to the equator. Ninety degrees is the point at which either the North or South Pole lies from the equator.

Using the protractor on your ball, mark off 45°, or one half the distance from the South Pole to the equator and one half the distance from the North Pole to the equator. At these points halfway between each pole and the equator and parallel to the equator, draw a circle around the ball. The circle between the equator and the North Pole is called 45° north latitude, and the circle between the South Pole and the equator is called 45° south latitude. All the corresponding degrees between 90° (at the poles) and the equator are referred to as *latitudes*. They form circles parallel to the equator.

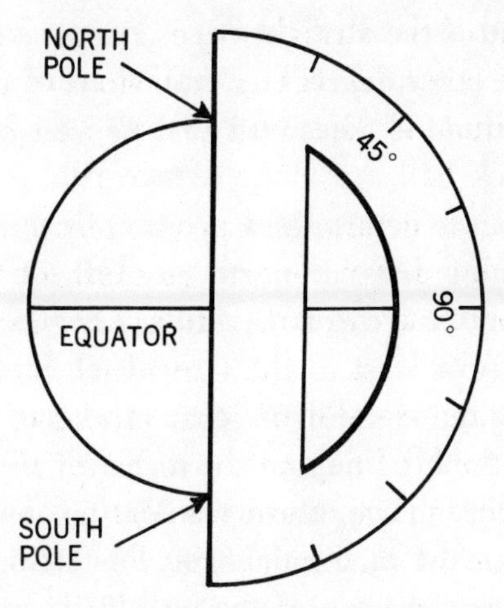

Since a latitude is a circle parallel to the equator, any given latitude alone does not fix a position. It merely states that the position under consideration is somewhere on that circle. If a navigator reported his position to the pilot as 49° north latitude, it would be like the visiting relative's saying, "I'm on Market Street." Since Market Street is essentially a long line traveling in a nearly east-west direction, his cousin would surely ask, "Market and *what?*"

To fix his position on the earth, the navigator must use another circle. Where these circles intersect (much like the circles that located the buried treasure), he will find his position.

On the circle you drew on your ball connecting the poles, ink in one of the semicircles that connects the poles. Call this 0° longitude (referred to as the Greenwich meridian, and so named after the town in England through which it passes). The other half of this circle will be longitude 180°. Lay the protractor on a table. Place the South Pole at the center point of the straight edge. Put Greenwich at 0° and think of the other degrees as extensions of degrees of longitude. Longitude is measured east or west of the Greenwich meridian.

Remember to determine a position by thinking of *latitude* as the angular distance north or south of the equator and measured on the arc of a meridian. *Longitude* is the angular distance east or west of the Greenwich meridian and measured along the equator or other circles of latitude.

We can think of degrees in terms of *time* and *distance.* For example, in *time*, there are 360° in a circle, and since the meridians of longitude extend by 180° both west and east of Greenwich, they make up a full 360°. If we divide the number of hours in a day, 24, into 360°, we get 15° for each hour. On the best map available, look up your approximate longitude and estimate your hours from Greenwich.

In *distance*, a land mile is 5,280 feet. A standard nautical mile is 6,080.27 feet. If every degree contains 60′ (sixty minutes) and if the circumference of the earth contains 21,600 nautical miles, compare this with the number of minutes in 360°. Can you find the radius of the earth in nautical miles when $C = 2\pi r$, (where C is the circumference and $\pi = 3.1416$).

CELESTIAL NAVIGATION

Whenever we look at the sky at night it appears to be a great dome above us with stars as points on this dome. Points on the earth's surface may be projected out into the sky and the sky above the earth's sphere may also be imagined as a celestial sphere. The earth's meridians and lines of latitude can also be projected upon this celestial sphere. The location of these points and lines on the celestial sphere is a basic technique of celestial navigation.

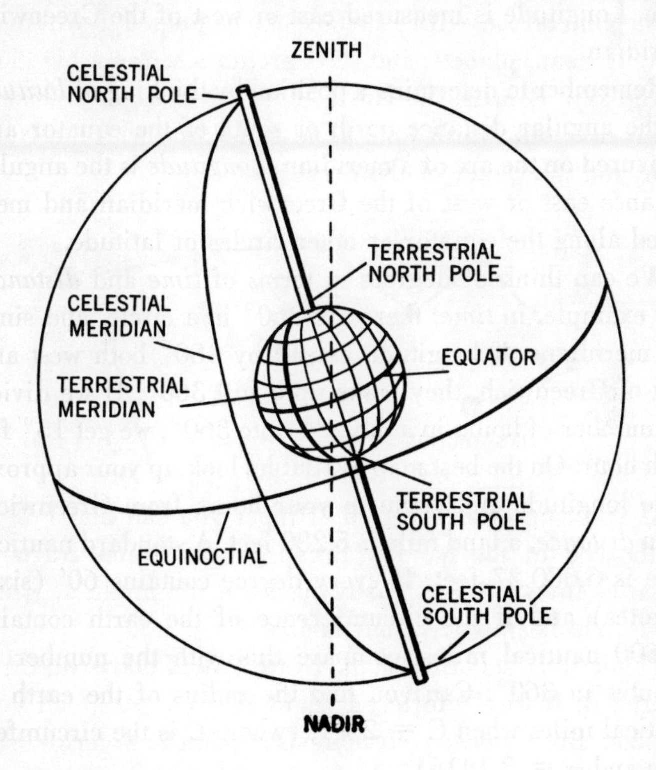

Celestial navigation is the science of determining a position on the earth's surface by means of observation of celestial bodies — the sun, moon, planets, or stars. Among the things needed to fix a position on the earth are a *sextant* (an instrument which measures the angle a star makes with the observer's horizon), a *chronometer* (or accurate clock), and a current *almanac* that gives the exact position of the stars in the celestial sphere.

The positions of the stars can be predicted for nearly ten years ahead, and the point at which they are directly over some point on the earth's surface can be judged to within 20 feet. The sun, planets, and stars are, in a sense, a big clock in the sky. Polaris, the North Star, for example, seems to hover over our North Pole almost in a line with the North Pole and the center of the earth.

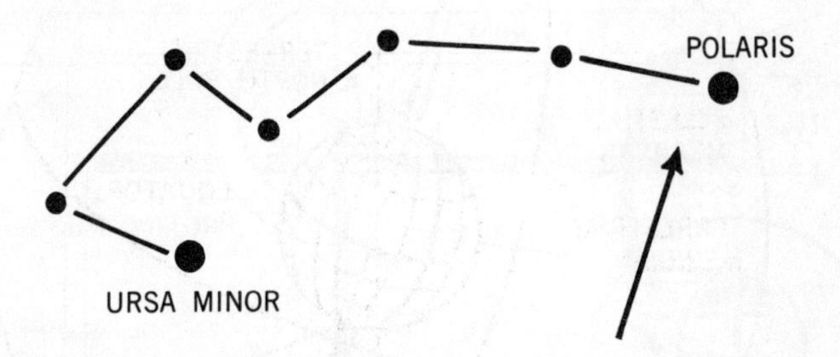

If you can locate the Little Dipper you can find Polaris at the end of the handle. Because light beams travel in parallel lines, we can easily measure the angle at which these light beams strike our houses.

If you were standing on the North Pole, Polaris would be overhead. It would form an angle of about 90° with your horizon. But suppose your home is at point 2. You can make a homemade astrolabe which uses the basic principles of the sextant and which can help you to get a fair measure of the angle that Polaris (or any other star) makes with your home.

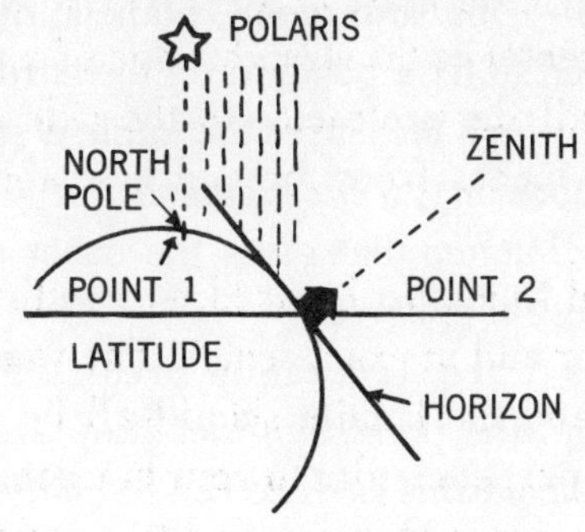

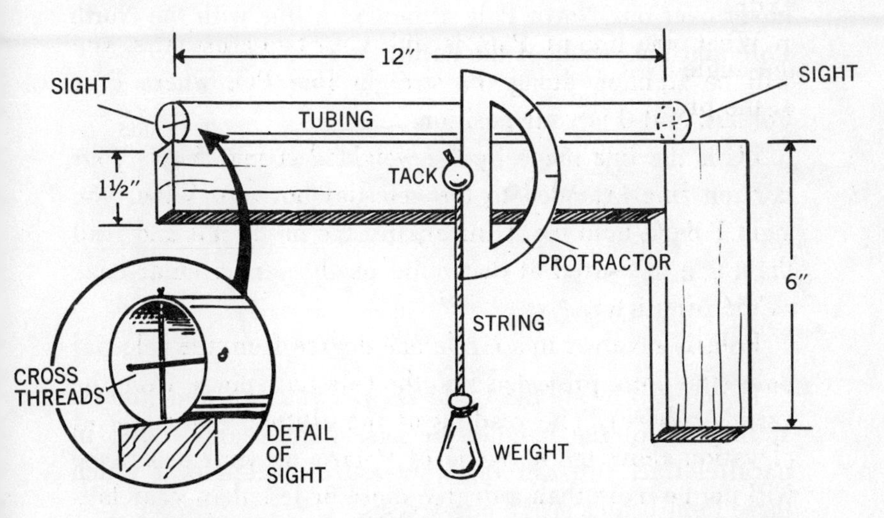

To construct this astrolabe, get a board 18 inches long, $1\frac{1}{2}$ inches wide, and 1 inch thick. Cut it into two sections: one 12 inches long, the other 6 inches long. Fit it together simulating a toy pistol. The 6-inch board will be the handle.

Tack in a cardboard tube on top of the 12-inch board and, using thread, put crosshairs across each end. The intersection of the crosshairs must be identical at each end of the tube. Find the center of the straight edge of a protractor, and at this point nail the protractor to the side of the 12-inch board about 6 inches from the end and about 3/4 inch in from the edge.

The weighted line must be fixed next to the straight edge of the protractor and at exact center. The weighted line, the straight edge, and the handle should all be set in parallel lines which are perpendicular to your horizon. This weighted line should be a piece of string tied to a weight of no more than 1 ounce. It will always be attracted to the center of the earth.

When you line up Polaris with your two crosshairs, you will be sighting along the straight line PO, where P is Polaris, and 0 is your position.

ZC is the line made by the weighted string. AB is your horizon line extended to the celestial horizon. When you sight Polaris hold the string against the protractor and read the angle measured at that point on the semicircular edge of the protractor.

Polaris revolves in a circle one degree from the celestial pole (the point projected into the celestial sphere from the earth's sphere). The reading of the altitude (or angle of elevation above the horizon) of Polaris on your protractor will not be more than a degree more or less than your latitude (or about 60 to 70 miles). You can be more accurate by taking a reading on the first of every month and then taking the mean altitude. You can check your observations against a good map on which your latitude may be located.

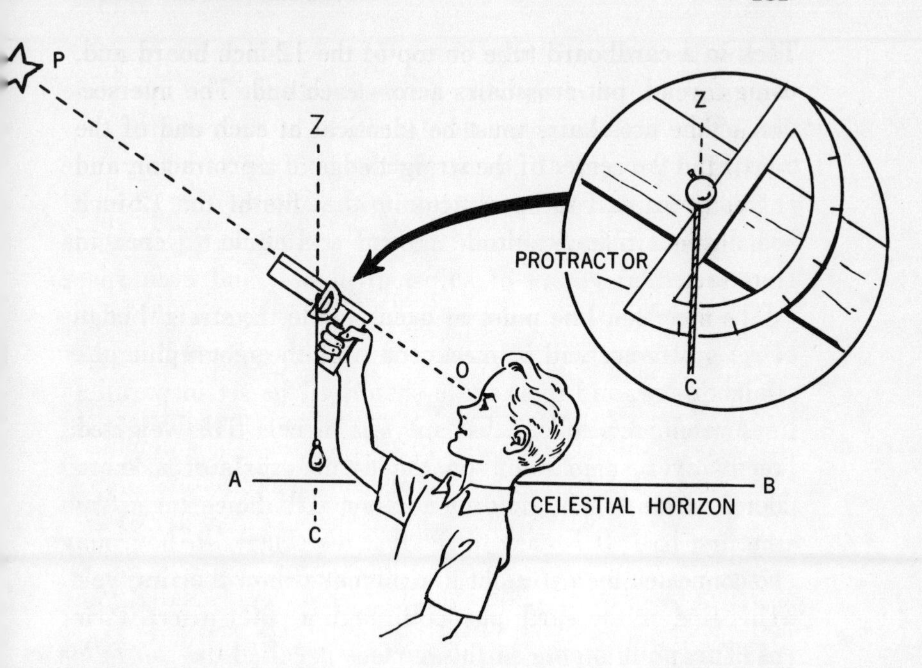

You can also estimate your own longitude by computing the number of hours between your time and Greenwich time. (If you call your local Coast Guard Station or Air Force Base, they might give you Greenwich time. Some radio stations also give Greenwich time.)

Noon is the time when the sun is directly over the meridian you are on. If a sundial registers noon one hour after it was noon at Greenwich, the earth has traveled 15° eastward. That point is 15° west of Greenwich. If our sundial registers noon on our meridian six hours after it has been noon on the Greenwich meridian, what time is it at Greenwich?

From the information given earlier, you should also be able to estimate the difference in miles between your meridian and Greenwich (measured at the equator). If you can determine your distance from Greenwich in this manner, you should also check your estimate with the best available map that will give you the longitude of your home.

In the process of estimating the latitude and longitude of your home, you have actually been finding the point at which the circle of latitude and the semicircle of longitude intersect. Navigators of ships, airplanes, and even space ships must find the point at which circles intersect, but the circles they use will be measured from the geographic positions of stars.

Astronomers tell us that any star or celestial body is directly over some point on the earth's surface. You can demonstrate this by holding another ball at any angle from the first ball. It is easy to see that the centers of both may be connected by a straight line no matter how they are held. This line on the earth passes through a point directly over us. This point on the earth's surface is called the *substellar point* of the star and often is referred to as the geographic position of that body.

In spite of refraction of light, "twinkling" (an effect of the earth's atmosphere), or uneven earthly motion, astronomers can predict for a given time that point on the surface of the earth which will have a certain star in its zenith. This *zenith point* is a point directly above the observer, or an altitude of 90°. For example, we learned that Polaris forms about a 90° angle with the North Pole. The zenith point of Polaris is over the North pole, at an altitude (angular distance) of about 90°.

The zenith of any place on earth is the point in the celestial sphere directly overhead. Conversely, the *nadir point* of a star is the point directly underneath it.

The *celestial horizon* is a great circle of the celestial sphere which is perpendicular to the zenith-nadir line at 90° from the zenith.

The *altitude* of a celestial body is measured by its angular distance above the celestial horizon. This angle is measured on a vertical circle which passes through the zenith and the celestial body.

If you hold your compass flat and line up north so that it matches the position of the north end of the needle, you will be able to mark off degrees on the celestial horizon using 0 at the north for a reference point. Can you locate the Big Dipper? Can you tell what bearing, or degree, on the compass the various stars in the Big Dipper make? At what degree or bearing is the house next door; your school?

The *azimuth* is the arc of a horizon measured clockwise between a fixed reference point (for example, the North Pole) and the vertical circle passing through the celestial body. When you located the angle of bearing of the stars in the Big Dipper you located its azimuth with the point of reference as the North Pole.

The *zenith distance* is the angular distance from the zenith measured on the vertical circle passing through the celestial body. It is equal to 90° minus the altitude of the celestial body.

The altitude or angular distance north or south of the celestial equator is called the *declination* (Dec.) of the celestial body.

The distance from the Greenwich celestial meridian is known as the *Greenwich Hour Angle* (GHA). Unlike longitude, it is measured westward from 0° to 360°. For example, the geographic position from Venus on Friday, April

22, 1960 at 10:00 A.M. is listed in an air almanac as follows: GHA 345° 11′. Dec. N 4° 55′. Of course, this position keeps changing because stars and planets, like the sun, are always traveling across the sky from west to east.

The *Local Hour Angle* is the difference in longitude between the meridian of a celestial body and the meridian of the observer. (It may be measured east or west of the observer so that the hour angle will not exceed 180° and must be indicated as east or west.)

Now that we have given you a list of terms, let's place them in corresponding order:

THE EARTH	CELESTIAL SPHERE
North Pole	North Celestial Pole
South Pole	South Celestial Pole
Equator	Equinoctial (Celestial Equator)
Latitude	Declination
Longitude	Greenwich Hour Angle
Difference of Longitude	Local Hour Angle
Bearing–Azimuth	Azimuth

With all these preparations, let us look at these things we have been discussing as they appear on the celestial sphere.

P is the Celestial Pole, M a Celestial Body, and Z is the Zenith of the observer's position. The local hour angle (measured at the pole) is ZPM. The angle PZM is the bearing or azimuth of the star.

If you look at this next illustration you can see that there are two triangles that have similar relationships to each other.

Remember that to every point or line on the earth's sur-

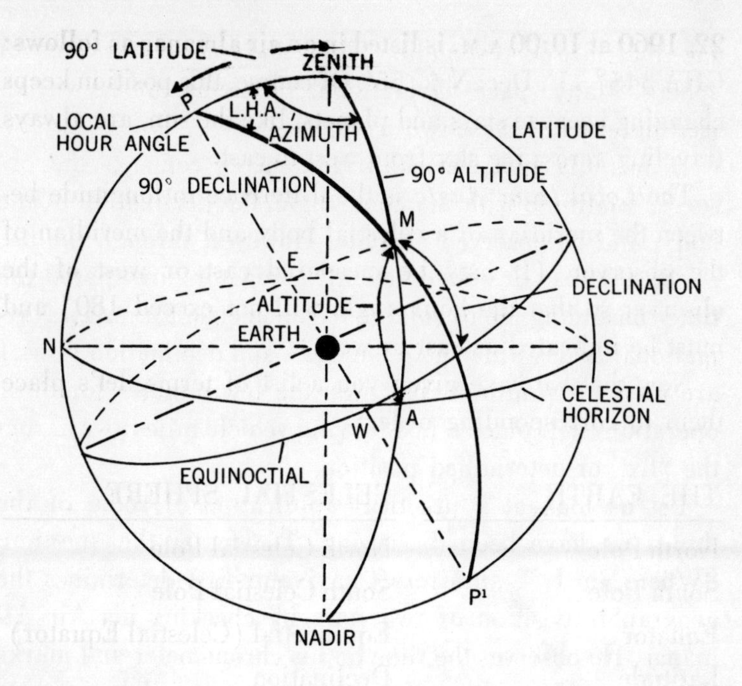
90° LATITUDE
ZENITH
P
L.H.A.
LOCAL
HOUR ANGLE
AZIMUTH
LATITUDE
90° DECLINATION
90° ALTITUDE
M
E
DECLINATION
ALTITUDE
EARTH
N
S
CELESTIAL
HORIZON
A
W
EQUINOCTIAL
P¹
NADIR

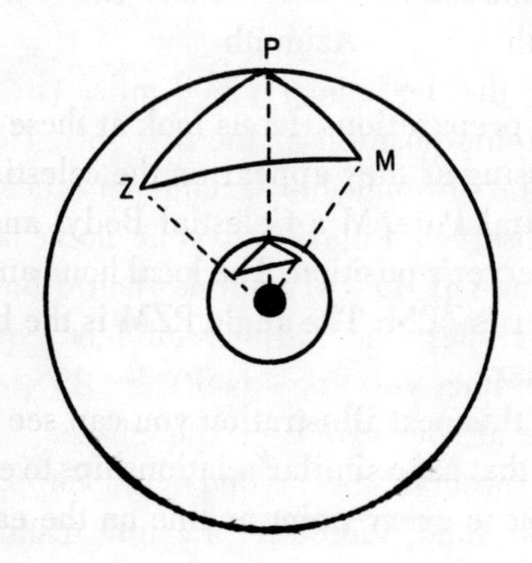
P
M
Z

face there are corresponding points and lines on the celestial sphere. Many space navigational problems can be visualized in terms of these two triangles.

A formula in spherical trigonometry connects the observer's latitude with the hour angle, the declination of the body, and its observed altitude. However, through the use of the almanac or epheremis, all navigators are spared the time-consuming job of solving trigonometric formulas. Navigational tables which give the GHA and declination (Dec.) are used for solutions, but even the few minutes for these operations will place a fast-moving vehicle miles away from the "fix" or determined position.

Let us look at a practical application of some of the things we have been discussing. To answer the question, "Where am I?", an aircraft navigator first determines the geographic position of two stars by checking his Air Almanac. He observes the time on his chronometer and marks the geographic positions for that instant on a globe or map. These points will be the centers of two intersecting circles, just as the rock and the well were centers of two intersecting circles.

Let us assume that he is nearly 300 miles (or 5°) away from the geographic position of the first star. He observes this particular star through his sextant (in much the same way that you observed Polaris on your homemade astrolabe) at an altitude of 85°. If a circle should be described upon a globe or chart the radius would be equal to the zenith distance, which you know is $90° - 85°$, or 5°. His position must be at some point on this circle.

Now he will observe the second star. Suppose it has an altitude of 84° and, therefore, a zenith distance of 6°.

One of the intersections of these two circles is the navigator's position. Do you remember the circles in locating the pirate's treasure? One intersection was disregarded because it was in the ocean. In this case, also, the navigator is able to disregard one of the intersections on the basis of his knowledge of his approximate position estimated or reckoned from the last time he took a "fix." To clarify this point, suppose the navigator of a plane knows that he is near Florida and one of the intersections is near the equator. He certainly will not fix his position near 0° latitude. Very often a third star is also observed to make the "fix" more accurate.

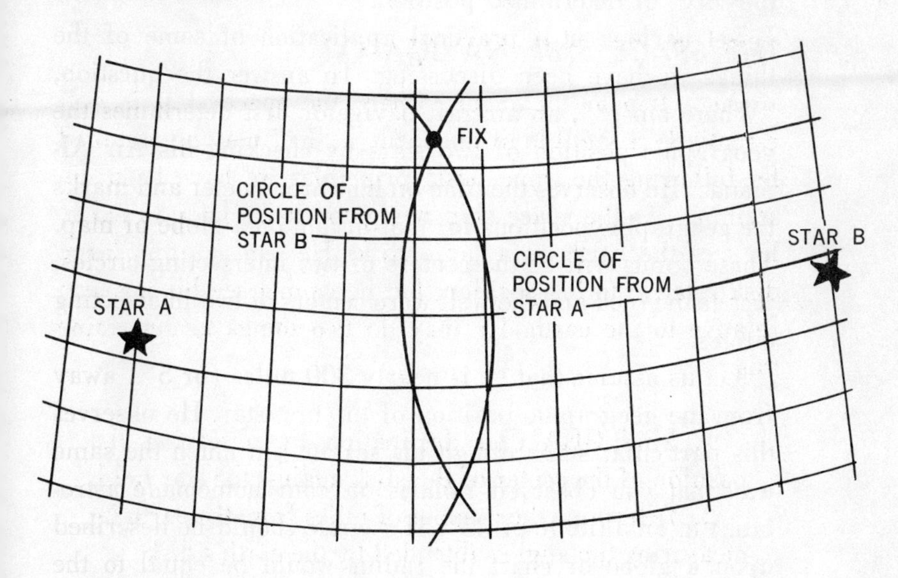

Computations must be accurate. Ships and planes have been lost as a result of poor work in arithmetic. Suppose a three-star "fix" at 20° west longitude and 65° north latitude took five minutes to accomplish and the plane was traveling at 360 miles per hour on a compass heading of 20° east of north. Can you estimate where the plane would be by the time the navigator had computed his position?

At speeds of nearly 18,000 miles per hour, or 5 miles per second, how far from the "fix" would a space ship be if a "fix" took one minute? Navigators of space ships must allow for the speed and direction of their ships over a period of minutes and integrate this estimate into the "fix." For speed in computations, navigators use simplified techniques, but all of these techniques are based on the principles used in the intersecting circles.

THE SPACE SHIP NAVIGATOR

On a trip to the moon, where the space ship is still essentially a satellite of the earth, a "fix" may be obtained by following the same basic principles we have been describing. As the space ship navigator looks back to earth, he sees the earth as a large disk. He can see this large disk relative to his position, but he cannot see his position relative to the earth. He may do two things to determine this:

1. Find GHA and declination by observing the position of the center of this disk against the star field.
2. Determine the number of miles from the earth by measuring the angle subtended by the earth's disk.

When the space navigator locates the center of the earth's sphere, he determines his nadir. When he establishes his nadir he also determines his vertical. Next, he reverses his line of sight along this vertical line and locates the zenith of the center of the earth's disk. If his zenith coincides with a star, all he has to do is use an almanac and determine that star's position for that instant to locate his position exactly. Otherwise, he can take sightings on two or three other stars and use the techniques of celestial navigation that we have just been describing to find out where he is.

A special instrument called a *bazooka telescope* helps him to locate optically both the center of the earth at nadir and the center of the star field at the corresponding zenith at the same time.

To determine his distance from the earth, he can solve the triangle by measuring the angle subtended by the earth's disk and solving the right triangle, where $R/D = \sin \frac{1}{2} A$ or $D = R \csc \frac{1}{2} A$.

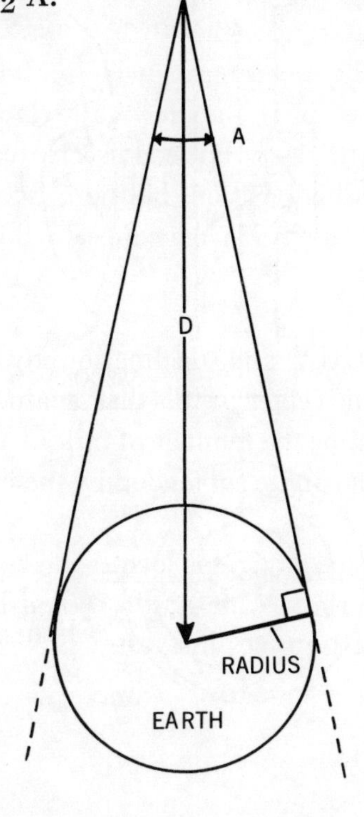

R is the earth's radius, D the distance from the earth's center, and A the subtended angle. The altitude above the earth's surface is: $a = D - R = R(\csc \frac{1}{2} A - 1)$. (The altitude, *a* in this case, is his distance above the earth's surface, not his angle from the earth.)

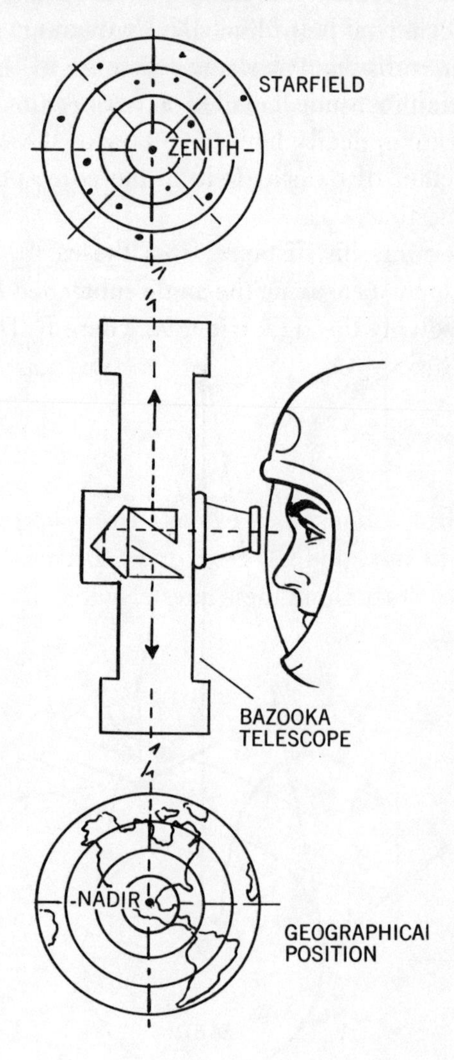

A ship at sea is considered to be moving in a two-dimensional plane. An airplane pilot also does his arithmetic for a two-dimensional problem and reads his height on an altimeter. A man shot up into space must solve a three-dimensional problem to answer "Where am I?" Mathematical formulas help him by expressing relationships between the subtended angle, the distance of the space ship from the earth's center, and the earth's radius.

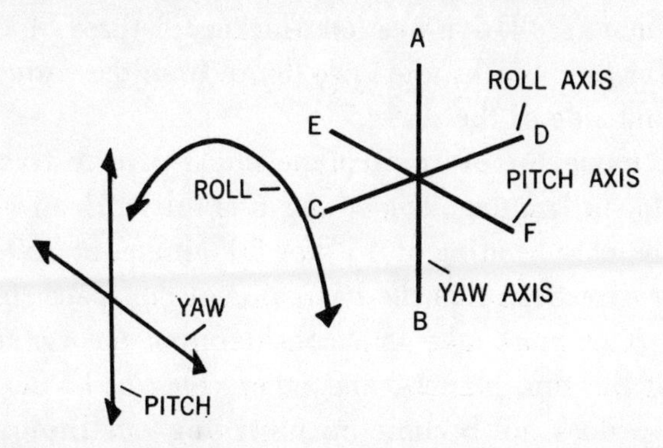

Axis AB is a line which extends from top to bottom, EF from side to side, and CD from front to back. The motions of the space craft along these axes are described in the next illustration.

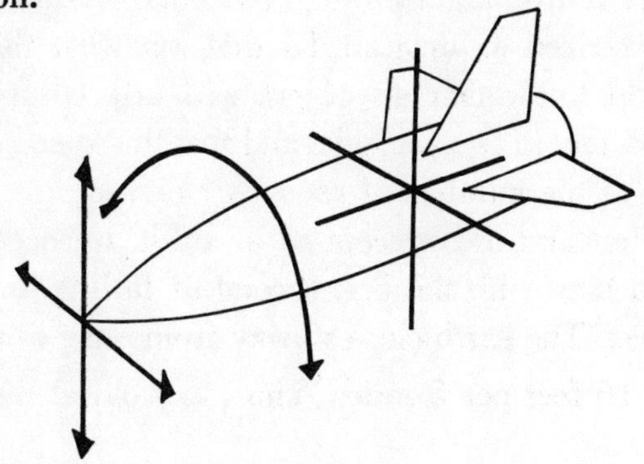

Small jet engines provide thrust in the appropriate directions to control yaw, pitch, and roll of space craft.

So far, we have been describing how the question "Where am I?" may be answered. Do you remember the second question the navigator must answer: "How do we get to our destination?"

As soon as the cousin knew the co-ordinates of 12th and Market, the out-of-town relative may have been given directions such as: "Drive west on Market for three blocks, turn right for four blocks, then two doors from the corner on the left-hand side of the street."

The navigator of an airplane might give instructions to the pilot in language something like this: "Head northeast on a compass heading of 45° for 50 minutes at 360 m.p.h."

Any directions that the navigator of the space ship gives to his pilot must take into consideration the gravitational pull of the sun, planets, and other celestial bodies so that his ship does not become an unwilling satellite of one of them.

Up to now, most of our space flights have been of the satellite type which have orbited the earth. Even in the immediate future, flight through our Solar System may well be characterized as orbital. To find out what this means, you should know that an object will fall 16 feet in one second, 64 feet in two seconds, and that this speed of falling increases as the number of seconds increase.

To understand the concept of an orbit, we need only be concerned here with the first second of falling, or with the first 16 feet. The earth curves away from our position to an extent of 16 feet per 5 miles. Thus, any object traveling at

5 miles per second is traveling forward and downward at the same time. Because of the curve of the earth, the object can continue in a circular orbit indefinitely until air friction slows it down and stops it.

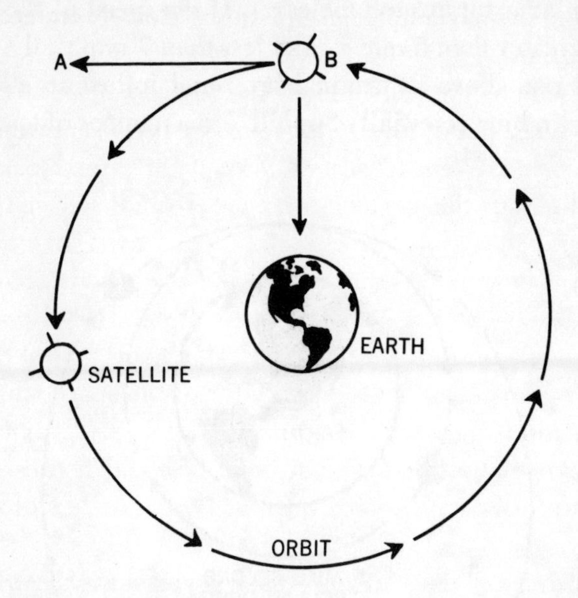

A satellite traveling above the earth's atmosphere is kept in orbit as the result of two forces: (1) the *earth's gravity*, which attracts the satellite to the center of the earth; and (2) at a proper velocity, the *satellite's inertia* of motion which acts along line AB.

To get the "feel" of these forces, you might tie a weight to a piece of string and swing it in a circular path over your head. The force pulling outward on the string would send the weight outward in a straight line if you released the string. By holding onto the string you are acting much like the gravitational force that holds the object in orbit.

When these forces are in equilibrium, the satellite will follow a circular path around the earth. Five miles per second is the minimum speed an object must attain to maintain a circular orbit around the earth. If the speed of the object were greater than 5 m.p.s., and less than 7 m.p.s., the object would rise above its original level and follow an elliptical path, climbing celestially "uphill," in a manner of speaking.

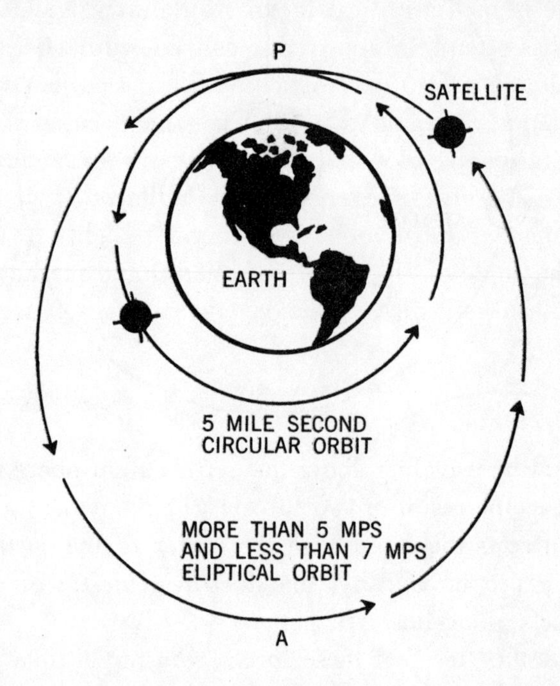

Perigee is that point nearest to the earth; apogee is the farthest point from the earth. As the space ship approaches apogee it slows down. As it approaches perigee it speeds up, reaching its original speed.

To make a rendezvous with another space ship, the navigator might wish to change his orbital radius. In such a situation, he would have to direct the pilot to effect an impulsive or even continuous thrust on the vehicle's rocket engine until the desired orbital radius was achieved. To complete a successful rendezvous or to effect a "collision" course with another planet, celestial co-ordinates and measures of distance are not the only factors to be considered.

Time is such a critical factor in planning a space flight that it has often been referred to as a co-ordinate. Take, for example, an orbit that is calculated for a collision course with Venus. Imagine that scientists have calculated that particular course of a space ship to Venus that requires the least expenditure of energy. At the moment of departure, the Venus-Sun-Earth angle is about 55°. Eighty-seven days after the angle of 55° is formed, Venus and the Earth will be at the instant of *conjunction* (the moment at which the

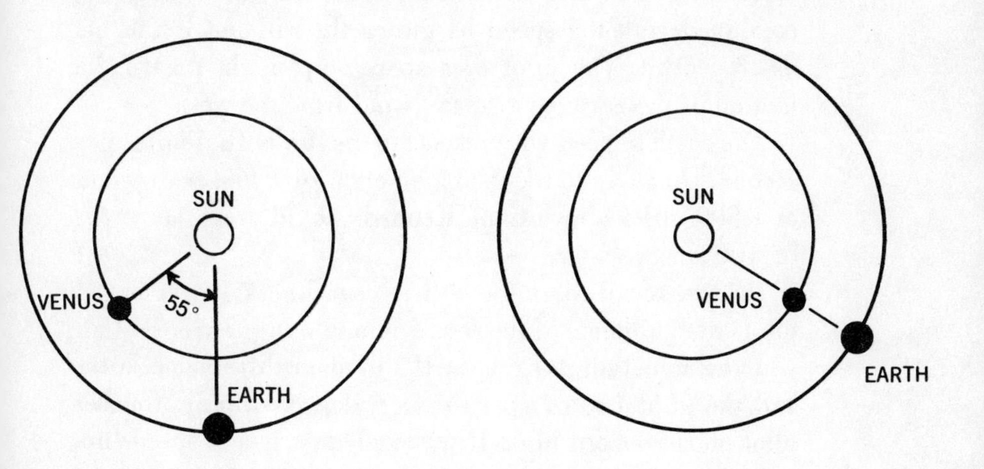

two bodies will occupy the position which makes a 180° angle on the Sun-Earth-Venus line). Another way of saying this is that a launching toward the conjunction point with Venus, based on an economical trajectory, is possible 87 days before conjunction. To make this collision course in 87 days, the space ship must leave precisely at a predetermined moment or risk tragic consequences. If it misses Venus, it is quite likely that the sun will be the master and the space ship will forever be in orbit as a satellite of the sun.

If these instants of conjunction are about 583 days apart, and one known conjunction took place on September 1, 1959, can you give the date for the next successive instant of conjunction?

The speed of the earth is another factor that must be considered in the timing of space voyages. Imagine how important the speed of the ship and of the wind are to an airplane taking off from an aircraft carrier. The space ship must leave the earth at such an angle that its own speed, combined with the speed of the earth, will put it into its desired orbit. The pilot of a space ship might regard the motion of the earth as a steady wind from the west.

The earth's speed with respect to the sun is 18.5 miles per second. On a trip to the moon, an error of 1 foot per second at 1,500 miles above Cape Kennedy could create an error of 100 miles.

Do you recall the pilot of the ocean liner? His essential job is the guidance of the vessel in and out of harbors. Can you see some similarities in the guidance of ocean liners and the guidance of space craft? Here is what the space pilot must concern himself with:

1. *Initial guidance* deals with the launching of the space

ship and the firing of the rocket engines. It is in this phase that the flight path of the space ship is determined.

One technique for the control of powered flight is called *inertial guidance.* This technique makes use of the sensitive instruments, called *accelerometers,* which are placed on three mutually perpendicular axes. The accelerometers detect changes in velocity of the space ship by measuring the effect of the earth's gravity on the inertia of the instrument. Because they are mounted on three mutually perpendicular axes, they can determine the path of the space ship in any direction.

2. *Midcourse guidance* is applied while the space ship is in free flight, which begins at *burnout,* or that moment when the rockets stop firing. Information on the space ship's orbit is relayed back to earth and into computers in the process known as *telemetering.* Following the path of the space ship by radio or with optical equipment is known as *tracking.*

3. *Terminal guidance* is concerned with the closing phase of the space voyage. It makes use of signals from the space ship's destination. These are sometimes signals of radar echo or heat radiation.

In the course of an orbital flight to Mars, a navigator might want to make a quick check on midcourse guidance. Simple geometry might be all the mathematics he needs. He can look up the position of the planets at any time in his almanac.

Assuming that the ship lies in nearly the same plane as the planets (except for Pluto, the planes of the orbits do not vary by more than 8°), suppose he observes the sun, earth, and Venus. The Sun-Venus line and the Sun-Earth line are

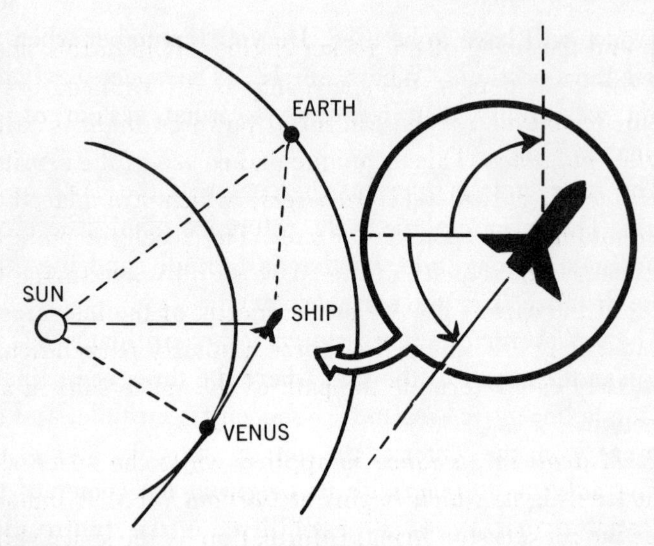

fixed (he can determine these lines by referring to his almanac). Using his sextant, he measures the angle between the Sun and the Earth, and the angle between the Sun and Venus. Simple geometry can then fix his position.

There are no roads in space. The paths to the stars must be found, not only through the observations of satellites and orbiting laboratories, but with the help of the men we send into space. Mathematics is one of the most important building blocks in preparing our astronauts for their voyages. Spherical trigonometry and geometry are not the only branches of mathematics they will be taught. Calculus, the whole study of ellipses and orbits, and vector geometry will become more and more important as man begins to find pathways in space.

In this chapter, we have been discussing a system of celestial co-ordinates with the earth at the center. But, when man reaches the moon and even beyond, other systems of reference will have to be used. Do you remember when we asked the question, "Where am I?" The space navigator might well reply, "In reference to what system of co-ordinates?"

The *geocentric system* has the center of the earth as its origin. The ecliptic plane is the reference plane where one co-ordinate is longitude, another is latitude, and the third is the distance from the earth's center.

The *heliocentric ecliptic system* of co-ordinates has its origin in the center of the sun, where the three co-ordinates are the heliocentric longitude, heliocentric latitude, and the distance from the center of the sun.

The *galactic system*, with its origin at the center of the Milky Way galaxy, is a possibility for the future. The galactic plane will be the reference plane, but a system of longitude and latitude co-ordinates must be chosen to orient it to the navigation of space ships.

Photography has some possibilities. With proper optical equipment, the space navigator could photograph the earth's disk against the star field. High-speed film can be developed in about 20 seconds. Transparent star charts could then be aligned over the photographs to enable navigators to scale off GHA and declination.

Whatever techniques prove to be the most effective means of space navigation, they will be techniques based on mathematical principles. Mathematics will find the pathways to the stars, because it is concerned with the study of the relationships of such things as distances, arcs, and angles. Mathematics can express these relationships in formulas or sets of instructions for tomorrow's restless adventurers.

AREAS UNDER THE NORMAL CURVE BETWEEN THE ORDINATE AT THE MEAN AND THE ORDINATE AT Z

expressed as proportions of the total area under the curve

Z	.00	.01	.02	.03	.04	.05	.06	.07	.08	.09
0.0	.0000	.0040	.0080	.0120	.0159	.0199	.0239	.0279	.0319	.0359
0.1	.0398	.0438	.0478	.0517	.0557	.0596	.0636	.0675	.0714	.0753
0.2	.0793	.0832	.0871	.0910	.0948	.0987	.1026	.1064	.1103	.1141
0.3	.1179	.1217	.1255	.1293	.1331	.1368	.1406	.1443	.1480	.1517
0.4	.1554	.1591	.1628	.1664	.1700	.1736	.1772	.1808	.1844	.1879
0.5	.1915	.1950	.1985	.2019	.2054	.2088	.2123	.2157	.2190	.2224
0.6	.2257	.2291	.2324	.2357	.2389	.2422	.2454	.2486	.2518	.2549
0.7	.2580	.2612	.2642	.2673	.2704	.2734	.2764	.2794	.2823	.2852
0.8	.2881	.2910	.2939	.2967	.2995	.3023	.3051	.3078	.3106	.3133
0.9	.3159	.3186	.3212	.3238	.3264	.3289	.3315	.3340	.3365	.3389
1.0	.3413	.3438	.3461	.3485	.3508	.3531	.3554	.3577	.3599	.3621
1.1	.3643	.3665	.3686	.3718	.3729	.3749	.3770	.3790	.3810	.3830
1.2	.3849	.3869	.3888	.3907	.3925	.3944	.3962	.3980	.3997	.4015
1.3	.4032	.4049	.4066	.4083	.4099	.4115	.4131	.4147	.4162	.4177
1.4	.4192	.4207	.4222	.4236	.4251	.4265	.4279	.4292	.4306	.4319
1.5	.4332	.4345	.4357	.4370	.4382	.4394	.4406	.4418	.4430	.4441
1.6	.4452	.4463	.4474	.4485	.4495	.4505	.4515	.4525	.4535	.4545
1.7	.4554	.4564	.4573	.4582	.4591	.4599	.4608	.4616	.4625	.4633
1.8	.4641	.4649	.4656	.4664	.4671	.4678	.4686	.4693	.4699	.4706
1.9	.4713	.4719	.4726	.4732	.4738	.4744	.4750	.4758	.4762	.4767
2.0	.4772	.4778	.4783	.4788	.4793	.4798	.4803	.4808	.4812	.4817
2.1	.4821	.4826	.4830	.4834	.4838	.4842	.4846	.4850	.4854	.4857
2.2	.4861	.4865	.4868	.4871	.4875	.4878	.4881	.4884	.4887	.4890
2.3	.4893	.4896	.4898	.4901	.4904	.4906	.4909	.4911	.4913	.4916
2.4	.4918	.4920	.4922	.4925	.4927	.4929	.4931	.4932	.4934	.4936
2.5	.4938	.4940	.4941	.4943	.4945	.4946	.4948	.4949	.4951	.4952
2.6	.4953	.4955	.4956	.4957	.4959	.4960	.4961	.4962	.4963	.4964
2.7	.4965	.4966	.4967	.4968	.4969	.4970	.4971	.4972	.4973	.4974
2.8	.4974	.4975	.4976	.4977	.4977	.4978	.4979	.4980	.4980	.4981
2.9	.4981	.4982	.4983	.4984	.4984	.4984	.4985	.4985	.4986	.4986
3.0	.49865									

ANSWERS TO PROBLEMS

Page 18

See the Code and match the *binary number* with the corresponding *alphabetic* character. Thus:

ALPHA CHARACTER	FIELD OF DOTS	BINARY NUMBER
T	● _ ● _ _	1 0 1 0 0
O	_ ● ● ● ●	0 1 1 1 1
D	_ _ ● _ _	0 0 1 0 0
A	_ _ _ _ ●	0 0 0 0 1
Y	● ● _ _ ●	1 1 0 0 1
S	● _ _ ● ●	1 0 0 1 1

Line indicates end of word.
Dots represent binary 1 in designated column.
No dots represent 0.
The binary message on page 18 decoded into alpha characters is:

TODAYS WORLD NEEDS TRAINED MINDS

CODE

DECIMAL	OCTAL	ALPHABETIC	BINARY
1	1	A	1
2	2	B	10
3	3	C	11
4	4	D	100
5	5	E	101
6	6	F	110
7	7	G	111
8	10	H	1000
9	11	I	1001
10	12	J	1010
11	13	K	1011
12	14	L	1100
13	15	M	1101
14	16	N	1110
15	17	O	1111
16	20	P	10000
17	21	Q	10001
18	22	R	10010
19	23	S	10011
20	24	T	10100
21	25	U	10101
22	26	V	10110
23	27	W	10111
24	30	X	11000
25	31	Y	11001
26	32	Z	11010

Page 20

Octal: 1357602 becomes:							
Binary (triples):	001,	011,	101,	111,	110,	000,	010
	1	3	5	7	6	0	2

Binary to Octal: 1011101 in triples 001, 011, 101
octal 1 3 5

Ans: 135 (octal)

11100001110011 in triples 011, 100, 001, 110, 011
octal 3 4 1 6 3

Ans: 34163 (octal)

11011111011110101011000
in triples 011, 011, 111, 011, 110, 101, 011, 000
octal 3 3 7 3 6 5 3 0

Ans: 33736530 (octal)

Page 21

Assumption: No wire on a *quinary abacus* can contain more than *four counting beads* after carrying. (Note that no wire on a decimal abacus can contain more than *nine counting beads*.)

Therefore: The highest number represented on a quinary abacus with *five wires* must be expressed by using *four counting beads* on each wire.

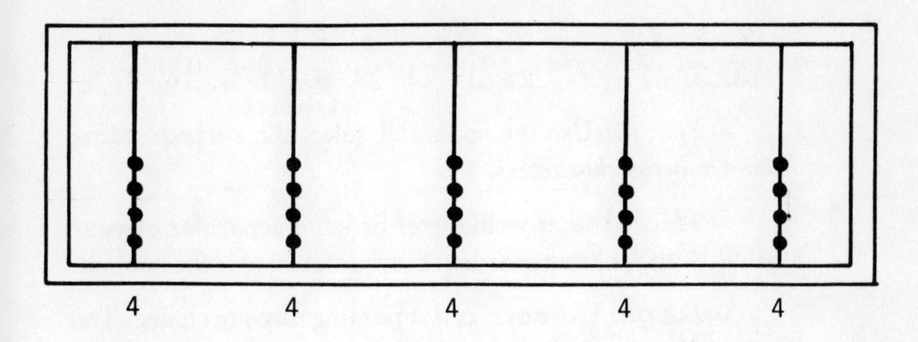

The quinary abacus can be represented thus:

$4 \times 625 \quad 4 \times 125 \quad 4 \times 25 \quad 4 \times 5 \quad 4 \times 1$

$2500 + 500 + 100 + 20 + 4 = 3124$

Ans. (in decimal notation): 3124

TERNARY PROBLEMS

1.

$$\begin{array}{r} 2 \\ +1 \\ \hline 10 \end{array} \qquad \begin{array}{r} 2102 \\ -101 \\ \hline 2001 \end{array} \qquad \begin{array}{r} 10221 \\ +11122 \\ \hline 22120 \end{array} \qquad \begin{array}{r} 11201 \\ +2100 \\ \hline 21001 \end{array}$$

2. Octal Message

First: Spell out the message in alpha characters:

M	A	T	H	E	M	A	T	I	C	S	I	S	A
15,	1,	24,	10,	5,	15,	1,	24,	11,	3,	23	11,	23	1

K	E	Y	T	O	S	C	I	E	N	C	E
13,	5,	31	24,	17	23,	3,	11,	5,	16,	3,	5

Second: Use the code and select the corresponding *numeric octal characters*.

Third: Use any character or letter separator of your choice — the character or letter separator here is the comma.

Fourth: Use any *word* separator of your choice. The straight line word-separator used here is the same as in the previous code: TODAYS | WORLD | NEEDS | TRAINED | MINDS.

Page 71

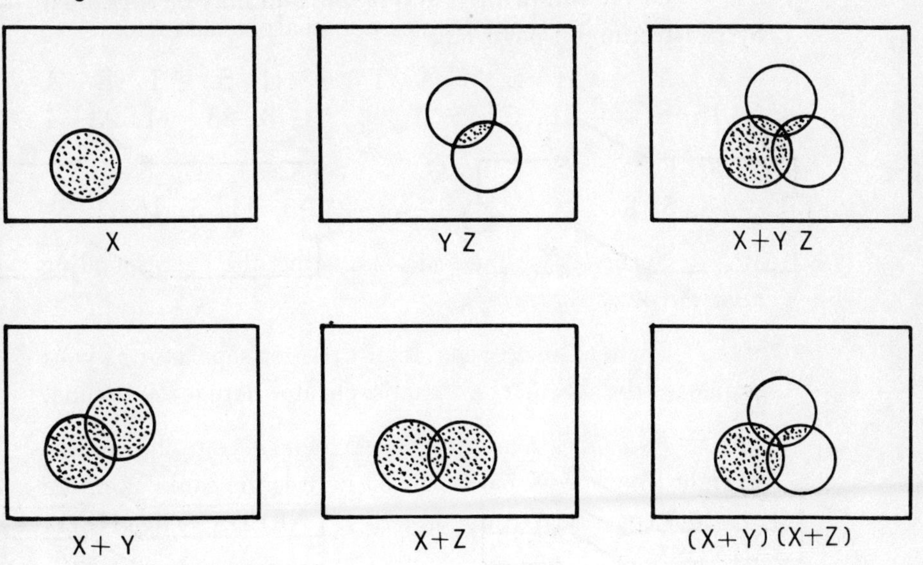

Because the two Venn diagrams on the extreme right are the same, we can say that addition is distributive with respect to multiplication. This is *not* a law for natural numbers. This *is* a law for classes.

1.

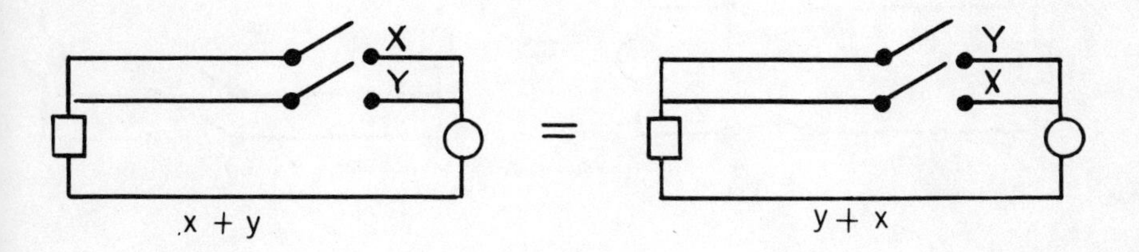

Or the following is acceptable and may be suggested by illustration on page 72:

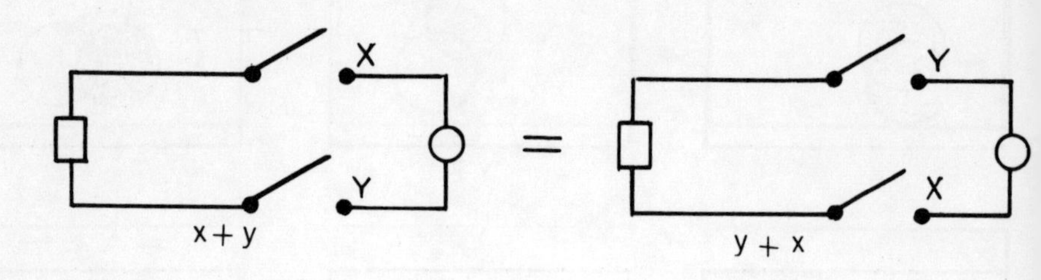

2.

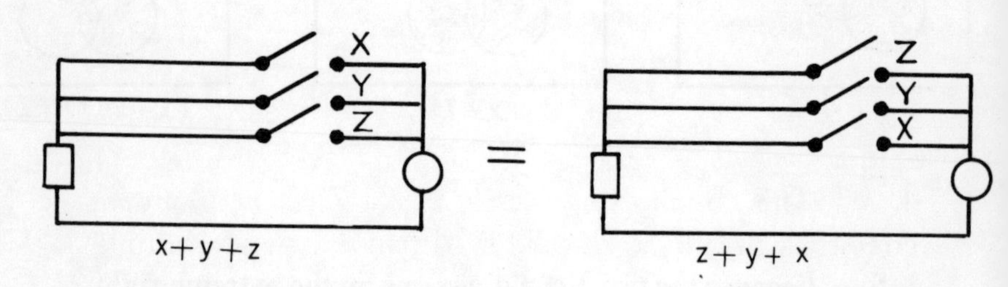

Or more properly expressed:

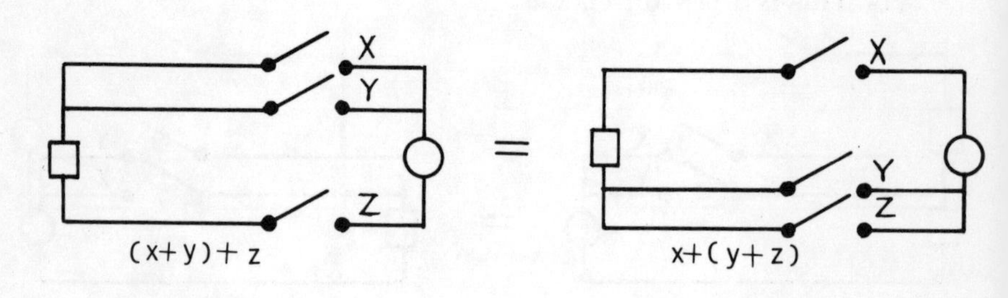

3. Commutative Law of Multiplication, XY = YX

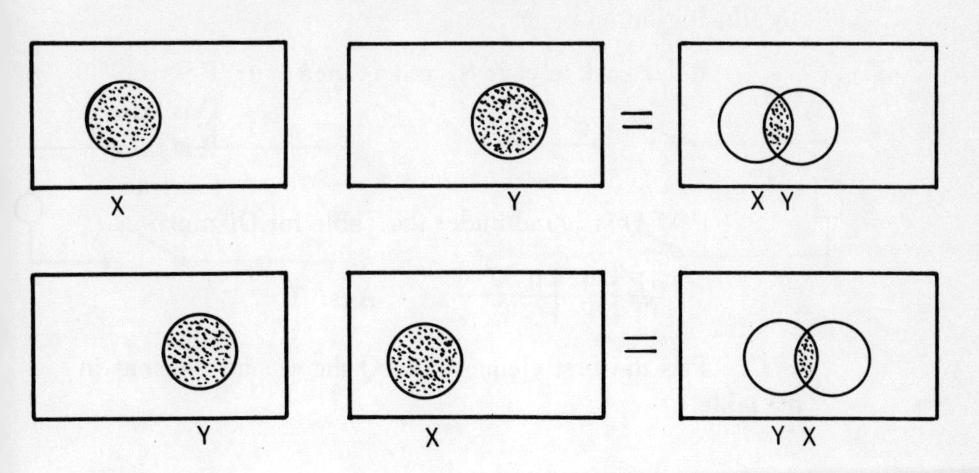

4. This circuit expresses (X + Y) Z. To get a proper circuit which will express the Distributive Law of Multiplication, the switching should be rearranged and preceded (or followed) by an additional circuit thus:

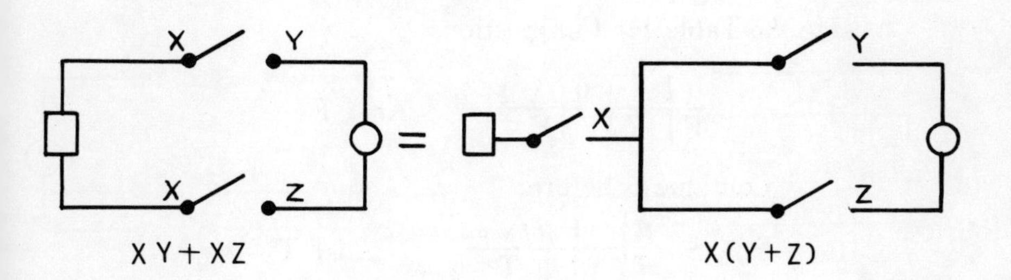

Page 88

Refer back to page 87 and assume that: P is true
Q is false
R is false
S is true

$P \vee Q$ is found under the Table for Disjunction.

p	q	$p \vee q$
T	F	T

Ans: T

P is the first element and Q the second element in the table.

Using Q as the first element and R as the second element and using the Table for Disjunction.

q	r	$q \vee r$
F	F	F

Ans: F

Using Q as the first element and R as the second and using the Table for Conjunctions.

q	r	$q \wedge r$
F	F	F

Ans: F

Continue as before:

$P \wedge S$

p	s	$p \wedge s$
T	T	T

Ans: T

$(P \wedge S) \vee Q$ First solve for $(P \wedge S)$, using the Conjunction Table.

p	s	$p \wedge s$
T	T	T

Then solve problem with $(P \wedge S)$ as the *first* element and Q as the second, using the Disjunction Table.

$p \wedge s$	q	$(p \wedge s) \vee q$
T	F	T

Ans: T

$(Q \wedge R)$ $(R \vee S)$

Find the truth value of $(Q \wedge R)$ which is F.

Find the truth value of $(R \vee S)$ which is T.

Consider $(Q \wedge R)$ the first element.

Consider $(R \vee S)$ the second element.

Refer to Disjunction Table.

$(q \wedge r)$	$(r \vee s)$	$(q \wedge r) \vee (r \vee s)$
F	T	T

Ans: T

Can you describe the circuit below in terms of a disjunctive sentence?

Let T be the ON condition of the switch.

Let F be the OFF condition of the switch.

Sentence: $P \vee Q$

Refer to the Truth Table for Disjunction. Three conditions will turn on the light:

P	Q	$P \vee Q$
T	T	T
T	F	T
F	T	T

Answers to problems on pages 94-96, and 98 will begin with an explanation of the solution to the first problem on page 96. It is suggested that you work out this problem first to help develop a systematic method of solving the other problems.

Page 96, line 19

$$[(P \vee Q) \wedge \sim P] \rightarrow Q$$

p	q	$(p \vee q)$	$[(p \vee q) \wedge \sim p]$	$[(p \vee q) \wedge \sim p] \rightarrow q$
T	T	T	F	T
T	F	T	F	T
F	T	T	T	T
F	F	F	F	T
		See Table for Disjunction	$(p \vee q)$ is the first element. p is second element. Negate second element and use Table for Conjunction.	$[(p \vee q) \wedge \sim p]$ is the first element. q is the second element. Use Conditional Truth Table.

Thus, this is a tautology. All T's in last column. Conclusion is valid.

Page 94

$$(\sim p \rightarrow q) \wedge \sim (p \wedge \sim r) \wedge [q \rightarrow (p \wedge r)] \rightarrow r$$

Use table bottom of page 91.

Ans: This *is* a tautology.

Page 95

1. $[(P \vee Q) \wedge \sim P] \rightarrow \sim Q$

p	q	$p \vee q$	$[(p \vee q) \wedge \sim p]$	$[(p \vee q) \wedge \sim p] \rightarrow \sim q$
T	T	T	F	T
T	F	T	F	T
F	T	T	T	F
F	F	F	F	T

Thus, this is *not* a tautology. There is one F in the last column.

2. $\{[P \wedge (P \rightarrow Q)] \wedge (Q \rightarrow R)\} \rightarrow R$

p	q	r	$p \rightarrow q$	$[p \wedge (p \rightarrow q)]$	$q \rightarrow r$	$\{[p \wedge (p \rightarrow q)] \wedge (q \rightarrow r)\}$	$\{[p \wedge (p \rightarrow q)] \wedge (q \rightarrow r)\} \rightarrow r$
T	T	T	T	T	T	T	T
T	T	F	T	T	F	F	T
T	F	T	F	F	T	F	T
T	F	F	F	F	T	F	T
F	T	T	T	F	T	F	T
F	T	F	T	F	F	F	T
F	F	T	T	F	T	F	T
F	F	F	T	F	T	F	T

This *is* a tautology. Conclusion is valid.

3. $P \rightarrow (P \vee Q)$

p	q	$p \vee q$	$p \rightarrow (p \vee q)$
T	T	T	T
T	F	T	T
F	T	T	T
F	F	F	T

This *is* a tautology. Conclusion is valid.

Page 96

HYPOTHESIS: 1. If it is raining, then the sky is cloudy.
2. It is raining.
CONCLUSION: ∴ The sky is cloudy.

HYPOTHESIS: 1. $P \rightarrow Q$
2. P
CONCLUSION: ∴ Q

$$[P \wedge (P \rightarrow Q)] \rightarrow Q$$

p	q	$p \rightarrow q$	$[p \wedge (p \rightarrow q)]$	$[p \wedge (p \rightarrow q)] \rightarrow q$
T	T	T	T	T
T	F	F	F	T
F	T	T	F	T
F	F	T	F	T
Same as Conditional Truth Table			P is the first element. $(p \rightarrow q)$ is the second element. Use the Conjunction Table.	$[p \wedge (p \rightarrow q)]$ is the first element. Q is the second element. Use Conditional Truth Table.

Yes, this is a tautology and the conclusion is valid. (All T's in last column.)

Page 98

Truth value for $Q \wedge R$ is false.
Truth value for $P \wedge R$ is false.
Note: Switch at R is open or in the *off* condition. Its truth value is F.

[If (Democrats have majority or Republicans debate) and Democrats do not have a majority] then Republicans debate.

p is a place holder for *Democrats have a majority.*

q is a place holder for *Republican debate.*

$$[(p \lor q) \land \sim p] \rightarrow q$$

p	q	$p \lor q$	$[(p \lor q) \land \sim p]$	$[(p \lor q) \land \sim p] \rightarrow q$
T	T	T	F	T
T	F	T	F	T
F	T	T	T	T
F	F	F	F	T

This *is* a tautology. Conclusion is valid.

Page 110

Using $V - A + R = 2$

The first network is a roadmap.

V = Cities

A = Roads connecting the cities

R = Regions (one outside the network and one inside the network)

Thus by Euler's Formula: $4 - 4 + 2 = 2$

First draw the streets. The network of streets which encircle and separate the buildings is shown below.

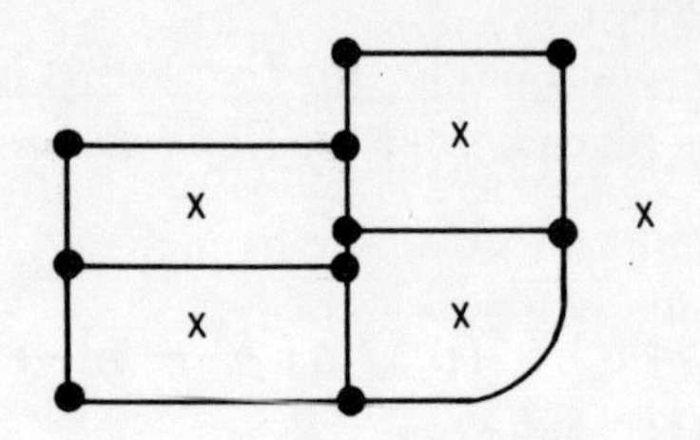

V = Street intersections, marked by dots.
A = Each line segment that connects two dots.
R = X (regions).

Thus by Euler's Formula: $10 - 13 + 5 = 2$

The New York City bridge problem reduces to:

$V = 6$
$A = 7$
$R = 3$

Thus by Euler's Formula: $6 - 7 + 3 = 2$

Page 113

Can of tomato juice (unopened) is like the sphere — a simple closed surface.

Fire hose is like a cylinder — a singly connected surface.

Baseball is like the sphere — a simple closed surface.
LP record is like the square — a simple surface.
Ice-cream cone
Full: Like the sphere — a simple closed surface.
Empty: Like the square — a simple surface.
Empty (with a hole in each end): Like a cylinder — a singly-connected surface.

The word *like* used in every answer refers to the fact that these surfaces can be topologically transformed into the surface equivalent of the objects they are compared to.

Page 170

9–1 expressed as a fraction is $9/10$ or 90% or .90. Look at the table on page 200.

From the *ordinate* at the *mean* and the *ordinate* at Z we must look up $\frac{1}{2}$ of .90 or .4500.

The closest value to this in the table is .4505, which corresponds to $Z = 1.65$.
Note: Z is expressed as the proportion of the *total* area under the curve.

19–1 equals $19/20$ or .95 probability.
$\frac{1}{2} \times .95$ is located on the Z scale as 1.96.

.98 equals $49/50$.
$\frac{1}{2} \times .98$ is 2.33 on the Z scale.

99– equals .99.
$\frac{1}{2} \times .99$ is 2.57 on the Z scale.

INDEX